FORESTRY COMMISSION BULLETIN
No. 48

Weeding in the Forest:
A Work Study Approach

By W. O. WITTERING, M.I.W.S.P., A.M.B.I.M., M.Inst.For.

Work Study Branch
Forestry Commission

A Membership Thesis for the
Institute of Work Study Practitioners

London: Her Majesty's Stationery Office
1974

A

ABSTRACT

In 1959, when the Forestry Commission's annual expenditure on weeding in the forest exceeded £1 million for the first time, the Work Study Branch was instructed to study the problem in all its aspects. Work was initially concentrated on hand weeding and the tools associated with it. Later studies of chemical and mechanical methods have resulted in the Commission adopting techniques which have given very substantial savings in costs.

At the end of eleven years of intensive effort, i.e. in 1970, the weeding account stood at £0·7 million. In real terms, allowing for the decreasing value of money resulting from inflation, a true saving of 44% overall (7·2% compound per annum) had been achieved.

Costs of the various methods of weeding are given together with advice on how to select the most suitable method. Protection of the worker is dealt with in detail.

New methods, such as ultra low volume spraying, which are being studied at present, are discussed.

ISBN   0   11   710140   0

FOREWORD

A Disclaimer

This Bulletin is aimed principally at the practical man, the man whose job it is to plan and supervise weeding in the forest. His attention is drawn to specific makes of equipment, and details of suppliers are given, with an indication of the cost. The mention of such products and services does not however constitute an official recommendation, endorsement or approval of any product or service to the exclusion of others which have not been mentioned and may be equally suitable. It is important to note that the Standard Time Tables and Output Guides in Appendix II were produced by the Forestry Commission especially for their conditions. The Commission can therefore accept no responsibility for any losses arising from their use (or misuse) in circumstances outside the Commission's jurisdiction

Enquiries About Products

The prices in this book were checked with manufacturers and were correct as far as it is possible to be on 1 August 1972. They do not include Value Added Tax. The Forestry Commission can accept no responsibility for any errors which may arise or any consequential losses arising from such errors. Readers are strongly advised to check all details with manufacturers before placing an order. Enquiries about products mentioned should be addressed to the firm concerned and not to the Forestry Commission.

Metrication

The Forestry Commission adopted metric measures on 15 February 1971 but it is appreciated that many other organisations have not done so. The principle adopted in this publication is as far as possible to give both measures, the ruling measure coming first, i.e. where a pressure gauge is graded in pounds per square inch, this measure precedes the metric equivalent. Similarly where planting has been carried out at 2·1 m spacing between the rows, the metric measure comes before the imperial. Forestry Commission standard time tables and output guides are produced in metric measures only. These tables (which are reproduced in Appendix II) and the costing data based on them in Chapters 21 and 22, are therefore given in metric terms only.

ACKNOWLEDGEMENTS

The work on which this Bulletin is based was carried out by many people between 1960 and 1972. The Author gratefully acknowledges the part they played in producing the information on which this Bulletin is based.

The photographs were taken as follows:

Plate 1 by courtesy of *Amateur Gardening*; Micron Sprayers Ltd, Plates Nos 58, 62 & 64; Cooper, Pegler & Co Ltd, Plate No 37; National Institute of Agricultural Engineering, Silsoe, Beds, Plate No 12; The Forestry Commission's Photographic Section, Plates Nos 5, 20, 44 and colour plate No 3; Mr W. E. Powell, Plates Nos 2, 3, 41, & 42; Mr F. B. W. Platt, Plates Nos, 8, 10, 11, & 32; Mr G. Bland-Flagg, Plates Nos 38, 40, 77, 78, & 79; Mr E. V. Rogers, Colour Plates Nos 1 and 2 and Plates Nos 39, 51, 55, 59, & 60; Mr D. H. Wallace, Plates Nos 14, 15, & 16; Mr J. Laurie Muir, Plate No 50; Mr D. J. Howard, Plates Nos 19, 22, & 25. All other photographs, including the colour pictures on the front cover and Colour Plates 4 & 5, were taken by the author.

The diagrams were redrawn by Alan Crow Associates from sketches by Work Study staff.

Mrs J. Anderson and Miss J. J. Sleigh typed the drafts.

CONTENTS

Contents *continued*

Contents *continued*

Contents *continued*

Contents *continued*

Contents *continued*

PART E: OTHER METHODS OF WEEDING

PART F: COSTING THE OPERATION AND CHOOSING THE METHOD

Contents *continued*

DIAGRAMS

Diagrams *continued*

COLOUR PLATES

BLACK AND WHITE PLATES

Black and White Plates *continued*

PART A
BASIC CONSIDERATIONS

1 Definition of Weeding

The Work Study practitioner defines weeding as "preventing competing vegetation from impairing the growth of the tree". The forester must then use his experience, skill and judgement to get as near to that situation as possible.

2 Cost

Before weeding there are a number of points to be taken into consideration and a number of questions which should be posed. One should estimate:

(a) The number of years for which weeding will be necessary.

(b) The number of times per annum that a compartment must be weeded.

(c) The intensity of weeding each time it is carried out.

With this information and the costing data given in Part F, one can estimate the total cost of weeding before the trees can be said to be established. As long as the money being spent is contributing to increased revenue from the crop, all is well. But where the return is adverse or marginal,* one should consider very carefully the need to weed at all, whether the intensity can be reduced, or whether a different, cheaper, method can be employed. In short, £1 invested must result in a return of more than £1.

3 Is it Necessary to Weed at all?

Will the growth of trees be impaired if I do not weed? If the answer is "no" then no weeding should be carried out. Supervisors should always be judging sites in the hope that they can wait until next year

before weeding. Sometimes weeding is done in a stand that is generally well above the weed cover, the object being to save a few weak "beat-ups" (replacement trees). Is it worth the money?

4 Can I weed by a Tractor Powered Machine?

As will be seen from the costs given in Part F, weeding by tractor powered machine is the cheapest technique and should be used where possible. If access by tractor is not possible then the next question should be answered.

5 Can I Weed with Herbicides?

Herbicides are cheaper than hand techniques but dearer than tractor powered machines. There may be reasons, e.g. amenity, why herbicides cannot be used – see Part D.

6 Are Two Weedings a Season Necessary?

It is common practice to weed small trees on bracken sites in June and then again at the end of August. In many cases a single later weeding in say early August may suffice. The major danger on bracken sites is of trees being smothered by bracken flattened in the winter. The later weeding removes this danger but poses the question of whether, by leaving the weeding until then, some trees would have suffered from bracken competition for light. Most tree species appear to stand up well under a bracken cover and only the most light-demanding species need to be freed twice in the season. With certain grasses, such as *Calamagrostis*, there is no doubt that two or even three weedings a season may be necessary if hand weeding is the only possible method.

---

*For more information on marginal costing, the reader is referred to *Forestry Planning* by Johnston, Grayson and Bradley, 1967.

B

PART B
HAND WEEDING

Chapter 1

TOOLS

1 General

In most circumstances hand weeding is more expensive than chemical or machine weeding (details of costs of the various methods are given in Part F). There are however still weeding situations which cannot be tackled by any other means than hand weeding such as areas unsuitable for machines and where the weeds are resistant to herbicides.

2 Tools Employed

During early studies on handweeding (in 1961), it very quickly became clear that a complete appraisal of tools suitable for hand weeding was necessary and specific recommendations were made. But edge tool manufacturers have reduced in number as mergers have taken place, and those remaining have rationalised their production lines so that well-known and much loved hooks of the past have disappeared from the catalogues; hence changes to the recommendations have been necessary on a number of occasions. Studies have shown that there is a best tool for each type of vegetation to be cut. Recommendations are given in Table 1.

TABLE 1

SUMMARY OF RECOMMENDED HOOKS FOR CUTTING SPECIFIED WEED TYPES

Weed type	Hook
Predominantly grasses, herbaceous weeds, rushes and bracken	Reap hook Dutch Weeding Scythe Bean hook
Woody weeds, climbers, bramble (i.e. up to one year's growth)	Light brushing hook S hook Bean hook
Heavy growth of woody weeds, climbers and bramble (i.e. more than one year's growth)	Heavy brushing hook S hook

3 Hooks and Scythes

These tools are now looked at in more detail:

(i) Reap Hooks (Plate 2)

The reap hook, also known as the sickle, bagging, fagging or paring hook, has a curved blade and a handle varying from 6–12 inches (15 to 30 cm).

Sometimes the handles are cranked and, where that is the case, different hooks are needed for left or right handed workers. This tool is suitable for cutting grass, herbaceous weeds, rushes, bracken and light coppice. The longer handles, 9 and 12 inches (23 cm and 30 cm), are useful when dealing with bramble, nettles, thistles, etc.

(ii) Dutch Weeding Scythe (Plate 3)

This tool resembles the agricultural scythe but is much smaller, the blade measuring only 12 inches (30 cm). It has a metal shaft with adjustable wooden handles and also a small additional curved blade for cutting the odd, thicker coppice shoots. This coppice hook is usually removed as it constitutes something of a safety hazard. The blade and the coppice hook are easily removed for sharpening or replacement by loosening two Allen screws by means of a key provided. The Dutch weeding scythe is preferred by some workers as an alternative to the reap hook and, as it is used in an upright instead of a bent position, ergonomically it is preferable. Proper training is essential with this scythe especially where workers are being converted from a reap hook.

(iii) Bean Hook (Plate 2)

This hook is similar to the reap hook but has a straighter blade and is of tougher construction. It is useful for dealing with the tougher grasses, rushes, bracken and herbaceous weeds and also light growth of bramble and coppice where a longer handle can be of value.

(iv) Light Brushing Hook (Plate 2)

There are many patterns of this hook and the blade shape varies from semi-circular, like a reap hook, to almost straight, rather like a slasher. It is essentially a long handled hook (24–36 inch (60–90 cm) handle) and is therefore useful for dealing with conditions where it is difficult to get in close, such as bramble, thorns, light coppice, climbers and mixtures of these with herbaceous weeds, grasses, etc. It is generally suited to one year's weed growth.

(v) Heavy Brushing Hook (Plate 2)

A heavier version of the light brushing hook with

less curve on the blade and generally more solid construction suitable for weeding in heavy woody weed conditions.

(vi) "S" Hook (Plate 4)

This tool is a cross between a heavy brushing hook and a billhook. It resulted from a staff suggestion by one of the workers at Ampthill Forest in Bed-fordshire where very heavy weed growth on the heavy clay was a major problem. It is suitable for weeding in conditions where otherwise a brushing hook would be used.

4 Suppliers of Hooks and Scythes

Table 2 lists the types of hooks and scythes used by the Forestry Commission and the current suppliers.

TABLE 2

HAND WEEDING HOOKS AND SCYTHES – SUPPLIERS AND PRICES

Type of Hook	Supplier	Description and Code Number	Size	Retail Price
Reap Hooks	Spear and Jackson (Tools) Ltd. St Paul's Road Wednesbury Staffs. WS10 9RA	Fussell Bristol Reap Hook 4700 No. 2	36cm blade 15cm handle	£1.75
	—— do ——	Fussell Fagging Hook 4709	38cm blade 23 cm handle	£2.25
Bean Hooks	—— do ——	Bean Hook 4707	39cm blade 15cm handle	£2.25
Light Brushing Hooks	—— do ——	General Pattern 4653	39cm blade 91cm handle	£3.55
	—— do ——	Light Pattern 4654	41cm blade 91cm handle	£3.55
	—— do ——	West Country Staff Hook 4655	38cm blade 91cm handle	£3.55
	—— do ——	General Pattern Brushing Hook 4606	38cm blade 76cm handle 91cm handle	£3.75 £3.95
Heavy Brushing Hooks	—— do ——	Irish Slasher 4605	40cm blade 76cm handle	£3.75
	Note: This hook is fitted with a ring and bolt for extra strength.			
	—— do ——	General Pattern Heavy Brushing Hook 4607	40cm blade 91cm handle	£3.95
Dutch Weeding Scythe	Koninklijke Nederlandsche Heidemaatschappij Postbus 33, Arnhem, Holland	Dutch Weeding Scythe Type VZ	30cm blade 140cm handle	about £6
'S' Hook	Bennett Ironwork 45 Nuffield Road Fleets Bridge Poole, Dorset	'S' Hook	32cm blade 48cm handle	£12.50 (£8.50 each for orders of 5 or more)

Chapter 2

TOOL MAINTENANCE

1 Cutting Edge

The opinion had long been widely held that an experienced worker knew instinctively when the cutting edge of his hook was correctly sharpened. To test this theory, measurement studies were carried out. Hooks were selected at random from workers at seven forests, the man being asked to sharpen the hook to his own personal degree of perfection. Using a two-way Vernier gauge, the thickness of the blades was measured at intervals of 50 mm along the blade and at depths varying by 0·5 mm from 1·5 mm to 7 mm from the edge. In all, 96 measurements were made for each hook. Graphs were drawn for each hook showing profiles at 50 mm intervals along the blade and a similar graph was drawn using average figures from the graphs of the individual hooks. Finally the mean profile was calculated and graphed. (See Diagram 1).

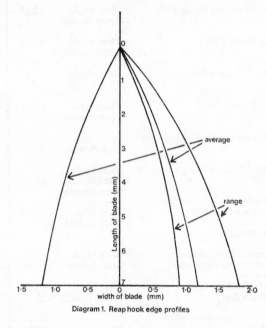

Diagram 1. Reap hook edge profiles

2 Gauge

As a result of the measurement studies, a gauge was produced from which the correct edge for a reap hook could be obtained as indicated by a V slot. Similar slots were also cut into the gauge for slashers, billhooks and axes. (See Plate 5). This gauge is now available commercially, see para 5.

3 Sharpening Stones (Plate 5)

Trials of various shapes of stone with varying degrees of coarseness showed that the most successful stone was a specially made boat-shaped stone 9″ x 1⅜″ x 1½″ (235 mm x 35 mm x 38 mm) and with two different faces, one of coarse material and one of fine material. For purchasing details see para 5.

4 Carrying Frog (Plate 5)

To complete the equipment required by a worker using a hook, a canvas frog which could be carried on the worker's belt and which would hold the stone and, in a separate compartment, the gauge was made and tested. This frog is available as shown in para 5.

5 Supplier of Tool Maintenance Equipment

Tool maintenance equipment as used by the Forestry Commission can be obtained as shown below:

Supplier	Description	Price
Stanton Hope Ltd 422 Westborough Rd. Westcliffe on Sea Essex	Medium/fine scythe stone Type 572 Edge tool gauge Carrying frog for stone and gauge	55p plus carriage

6 Replacement of Worn Hooks and Sharpening Stones

Hooks and sharpening stones are cheap in relation to the cost of the work they do. If a reap hook costing about £2 lasts one weeding season (say 6 months) then it represents less than ½% of the total weeding cost or about 7·5p per hectare. It follows therefore that money can be saved by discarding worn or defective hooks. The cost of the sharpening stone per hectare is infinitesimal and it is most important that broken stones should be replaced to reduce minor accidents. Supervisors have been known, convinced that they were saving money, deliberately to break stones in half and issue the pieces!

Chapter 3
FACTORS AFFECTING THE JOB

1 Training

Adequate training in hand weeding, particularly with reference to the correct use of the hook, proper maintenance and correct working method, is essential and can play an important part in keeping costs to a minimum.

2 Producing a Standard Time Table

Hand weeding is one of the most comprehensively studied jobs in forestry, not only with reference to method of working but also to the establishment of standard time tables which form a solid basis for a piece rate scheme. The hand weeding standard time table has evolved over the years from initial studies in North Wales in 1961. After thorough trials in Southern and Eastern England in 1963 and in 1964, the second edition was produced (1965) which was acceptable in the very different conditions of North Scotland. Since then, a third edition (1969—revised 1973) has emerged from re-studies in South Western England and is reproduced in Appendix II, page 96.

3 Factors Affecting Working Time

Producing a standard time table for hand weeding was difficult as it is one of the few jobs in forestry where the trees themselves play only a minor part in the job. In production work, the factors which have most influence on the time taken to do a job can be measured, e.g. the size of tree or length of haul. With weeding, on the other hand, there are numerous factors which can affect working time and very few of them can be measured easily. Consequently a partially subjective method for assessing weed growth has had to be adopted in order to establish standard times. The major factors which affect the working time have been recognised and isolated; these factors are assessed, or wherever possible measured, and a standard time is allocated to each which contributes to the total time for the job. This method is basically the same as that used intuitively by an experienced supervisor when he prices a job, but the Work Study scheme attempts to codify and rationalise the assessment so that supervisors setting weeding rates for the first time will find their job easier. The following factors have a major influence on working time:

(i) Weed Species and Density

Four major weed groups are recognised:

(A) Bracken and Herbaceous Plants, most Soft Grasses.

(B) Coarse Grasses and Rushes.

(C) Climbers ⎫ one year's growth only, but
(D) Woody Weeds ⎭ see (viii)

Group A is the easiest to cut and Group D the hardest. There are, of course, wide differences of size, thickness and toughness within each group depending on the time of the year, site fertility, aspect, rainfall, etc. An attempt has been made to overcome this problem by splitting each major weed group into three grades of difficulty, viz:

(1) Light

(2) Moderate

(3) Heavy

The Appendix to the Standard Time Table, page 102, describes in detail the method of allocating a grade to the different weed groups. A range of measurements, an indication of the density of stems, and a general description are used to identify each grade.

(ii) Cover

Generally the major weed groups occur in mixtures and it is necessary to estimate the percentage cover of each weed group. A typical assessment might be:

Bracken	60%
Rush	10%
Woody Weeds (coppice)	20%
Bare ground, i.e. weeding not required	10%
Total	100%

(iii) Spacing

Spacing of trees affects weeding time in two ways. Firstly in relatively wide spacings, e.g. 2·1 m (7′), it is usually possible to leave an uncut strip between the rows, thus reducing the area to be weeded, while in closer spacings it is often necessary to cut all the weed growth. Secondly, the worker's pace is checked when he cuts around a tree, there are more checks in close spacings and also more rows within a given area.

(iv) Slope

On slopes up to about 25%, a man can work downhill almost as easily as on level ground and his working position cutting uphill is slightly better than on the level. However, on steeper slopes it becomes increasingly difficult to move easily and fatigue is greater. On slopes steeper than 25% it is usually necessary to work uphill only and extra time is needed to walk down the hill. On steep, unstable slopes it is difficult to move rhythmically.

(v) Surface

Rocks and stones interfere with working rhythm and usually increase sharpening time. Windrows of slash and fallen branches from bark-ringed overhead cover also make work more difficult.

(vi) Size of Tree

Small trees under a dense weed cover are often difficult to see. Particular examples are Norway spruce under grass, or oak under a weed cover of coppice and herbaceous plants.

(vii) Ploughed Sites

In general, weeding is quicker on ploughed sites because it is only necessary to cut a narrow strip of weed growth around the trees on top of the ridge. Sometimes the converse is true, unstable ridges make it necessary to work from the furrows; this forces the worker to cut a half strip of weeds to left and right and the furrows may be choked with gorse and bramble making movement difficult.

(viii) More than One Season's Growth

The standard times are for sites which have been weeded annually. On sites where weeding has been left for a year or two, woody weeds, climbers and coarse grasses taken longer to cut.

(ix) Exceptional Growth

Very moist and fertile sites will in some seasons produce a weed growth heavier than the "heavy" grade recognised. This is particularly true of herbaceous plants; bracken and willow herb sometimes grow to 7′ (2·0 m) or more by the end of summer.

4 Constant Factors

Of all these factors, the first three (i.e. weed species and density, cover and spacing) are the most im-portant factors; they are used to determine the standard time and therefore the piece work rate, and so they must be assessed carefully for every site. All other factors affecting working time have been isolated and described in paragraph 7 of the Standard Time Table – Modifications and Variations – and are applied as additions or deductions from the standard times, based on the three main factors, shown in paragraph 6 of the table.

5 Introducing a Piece Work Scheme

Readers who intend to introduce their own piece work scheme based on this Standard Time Table are advised to read the table carefully and become thoroughly conversant with Appendix 1 to this bulletin, where the layout of a table is described in detail, as is the method of converting time to money.

6 Weed Types not Covered by the Hand Weeding Table

The following weed types and techniques have not yet been studied:

 (a) Heather

 (b) Trampling as opposed to cutting

 (c) Very little work has been done on bracken whipping, insufficient to publish at this stage.

7 Winter Weeding and Cleaning

Trees which are several years old and above the general level of grass and herbaceous weeds suffer from the competition of coppice regrowth, bramble, and on some sites, honeysuckle and traveller's joy. If weeding is delayed until late Winter/early Spring, costs are reduced because only the woody growth and climbers need cutting. On sites where windblow of young Douglas fir is a possibility, winter weeding should be carried out in dry periods, and early spring is often suitable.

A limited amount of work has been carried out on winter weeding and cleaning and a standard time table has been produced. This table is reproduced in Appendix II, page 118. The method of use is very similar to the table for hand weeding.

PART C
WEEDING WITH MACHINES

Chapter 4
MACHINE WEEDING: GENERAL

1 Introductory

The Forestry Commission Work Study Branch has been studying weeding machinery for the past eight years. In that time, with one or two exceptions (including of course the portable brushcutter and grass roller), no "custom-built" forestry weeding machine has emerged. All machinery seen has been built with something else (generally agriculture) in mind. This is a source of disappointment to the author for here lies the possibility of the cheapest method of weeding but which has failed to achieve the potentially low costs because of inadequate equipment.

2 Scrub Clearance and Cleaning

The work carried out with machinery has been mainly in the weeding sphere, but there have also been improvements in scrub clearance and cleaning techniques. Weeding is generally a lighter job than scrub clearance and cleaning and persons choosing to do the latter with equipment listed in the following pages must not be disappointed if their machines do not fulfil a function for which they were not designed.

3 Types of Machine

Basically, weeding machines fall into three categories:
   a. Portable, i.e. carried by the operator (see Chapter 5)
   b. Pedestrian controlled (see Chapter 6)
   c. Tractor powered (see Chapter 7)

4 Types of Cutting Head

Methods of cutting vary. Each is described below:

(a) Rotating Saw Blade

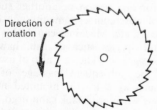

Diagram 2. Rotating saw blade

This blade requires little explanation. It is simply a circular saw blade rotating on the end of a shaft. The type of guard used is of some importance as is the direction of rotation.

(b) Rotating Grass Blade

A flat metal plate, usually three or four sided, with the corners sharpened. See Chapter 5, para 5, page 9, and Diagram 3.

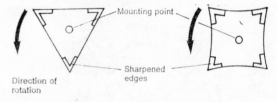

Diagram 3. Rotating grass blades

(c) Rotating Bar; Rigid Type

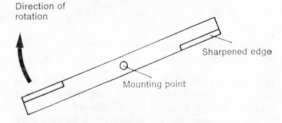

Diagram 4. Rotating bar: rigid type

A bar of metal with two sharpened edges which rotates to cut the weed growth. Considerable shock can be transmitted to the machine and tractor gear boxes if, for example, the blade hits a stump, unless certain precautions are taken. See Chapter 7 para 7(ii). The mounting point is liable to clog with vegetation. These blades are relatively expensive.

(d) Rotating Bar: Free swinging

An improvement on the previous type; shock to the gearbox and tractor is reduced by the free swinging blades which cost less but there is still the possibility of clogging. This method is of value if variations in cutting width are required.

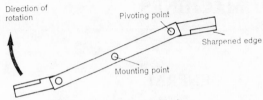

Diagram 5. Rotating bar: free swinging

Note: Free-swinging blades put large out-of-balance forces on the cutter when one blade swings back; consequently the gearbox and cutter have to be of heavier construction to withstand these forces.

(e) Rotating Saucer with Free Swinging Blades

Section

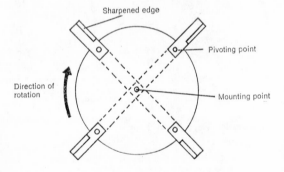

Diagram 6. Rotating saucer with free swinging blades

Two or four blades

The central part of the bar in (d) is welded to a saucer-like fitment with two or four free swinging blades mounted. There is less likelihood of damage by hitting stumps for the saucer tends to ride over them and the danger of the drive shaft clogging with vegetation is greatly reduced. (See para 4(d) for note about free swinging blades.)

(f) Rotating Chains

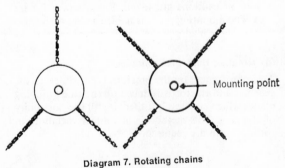

Mounting point

Diagram 7. Rotating chains

Chains are quite suitable for cutting grass, bracken and herbaceous weeds, but a blade is better for dealing with a predominance of woody weed growth.

(g) Reciprocating Blade

Diagram 8. Reciprocating blades

Two pieces of metal with a series of sharpened serrations are moved backwards and forwards across each other and cut rather like many pairs of scissors. Sometimes one is fixed and the other moves. Very useful for grass cutting but limited in the size of woody growth they can cut.

(h) Flails

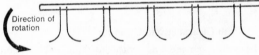

Diagram 9. Flails   Sectional view

The only cutting head which rotates vertically, all the others cutting in a horizontal plane. This type of head is also of value when chopping material which has already been cut and is laying flat as for example brash on a clear-fell area. It also has advantages in that it reduces the length of a weeding machine and makes design work simpler. It can be more difficult to repair than other heads. The flails are free swinging and a number of different shapes of flail are made. (See note about free-swinging blades in para 4(d).)

5   The Place of Machines in the Weeding Armoury

In spite of the availability of herbicides, there are circumstances in which the use of weeding machines, in particular the tractor powered variety, emerges as the cheapest method of weed control. There are also situations in which herbicides cannot be used or are ineffective for one reason or another such, as the proximity of watercourses, amenity considerations, resistant weeds, etc. Machines can deal with chemically difficult species such as ash, hawthorn, or *Calamagrostis* grasses. They are also of use in cutting racks for the subsequent passage of spraying machines such as a tractor mounted mistblower. In conditions where a tractor cannot go, it may be possible to use a pedestrian controlled machine. Certain ground conditions, such as slopes of over 25% and very boggy ground, automatically rule out the use of any form of wheeled weeding machine.

Chapter 5

PORTABLE BRUSHCUTTERS

1 Description

A portable brushcutter (also known as a portable clearing saw) consists of a small petrol engine usually driving a circular saw blade through a driving shaft. The driving shaft can be rigid or flexible and if the former, can be one piece or two pieces. There are a number of different types of blade available and different types of guard.

2 Machine Tests

There are so many makes on the market that trials by the Forestry Commission's Work Study Branch were limited to testing principles, mainly the following different methods of driving the cutting head:

(a) one piece driving shaft
(b) two piece driving shaft
(c) flexible driving shaft
(d) machine convertible from chainsaw
(e) flexible drive from engine mounted on a small wheeled trolley (not strictly a portable machine).

This chapter is based to a great extent on the results of these trials.

3 Types of Driving Shaft

The advantage claimed for a two piece shaft is that it makes transportation and servicing easier. There is little difficulty in transporting any portable brushcutter in a forest vehicle and the extra linkage required can if anything increase the need for servicing because of wear at that point. Hence a machine with a one piece shaft is recommended. It was found with flexible drive machines, that, generally speaking, considerable breakage of the shafts could be expected with the resultant high cost and down time whilst undergoing repair. They are not therefore recommended, except in special circumstances, see paragraph 8.

4 Direction of Rotation of Blade

The direction the blade rotates is of some importance. All machines are suspended from the operator's right shoulder thus it is best to swing the machine from the right to the left when cutting. Hence an anti-clockwise rotating blade will tend to cut into the weed growth instead of shearing away from it.

5 Blade Types

All brushcutters are supplied with a circular saw blade (Diag 2) which is used when the weed growth is predominantly woody material. Most machines are also supplied with a special head designed for grass cutting such as shown in Diagrams 3 and 4 and Plate 7. These blades are of limited value; the use of a portable brushcutter for controlling grasses, bracken or herbaceous weeds is expensive and at present is not recommended. Attempts to cut woody vegetation with the grass blade is likely to result in damage to the machine. The circular saw blade quickly becomes clogged when cutting grasses and herbs which occur in mixture with woody growth unless a modified guard (para 7) is fitted. Use of the saw blade only, saves time in changing blades and prevents straining the machine. The saw blades take longer to sharpen and set than the grass cutting blades.

6 The Machine

The type of machine recommended therefore is one having a rigid drive shaft and an anti-clockwise rotating blade. One can add "good spares facilities". The Forestry Commission uses the Husqvarna 65 clearing saw—see Plate 6.

Supplier	Description
Hyett Adams, Ltd.	Husqvarna 65 clearing
Stonehouse	saw
Gloucestershire	*Price*
GL10 2JB	£124

This saw can also be built up from a Husqvarna A65 chainsaw by means of a Husqvarna clearing saw conversion kit. This is an advantage when there is limited use for both machines. The cost of the conversion kit is £79.

7 Blade Guards

The type of guard is of paramount importance. Plate 8 shows a close fitting type of guard often supplied with a saw. If a piece of woody material gets caught between the blade and the guard, it can jam and accidents can happen if operators try to remove the obstruction without first stopping the saw. Grass can wrap itself around the blade spindle also causing stoppage and is difficult to remove. Hence, a modified guard is recommended. Some suppliers sell them as standard equipment, but if not, they are easily made. Plate 9 shows the guard supplied with the Stihl brushcutter. The Work Study Branch

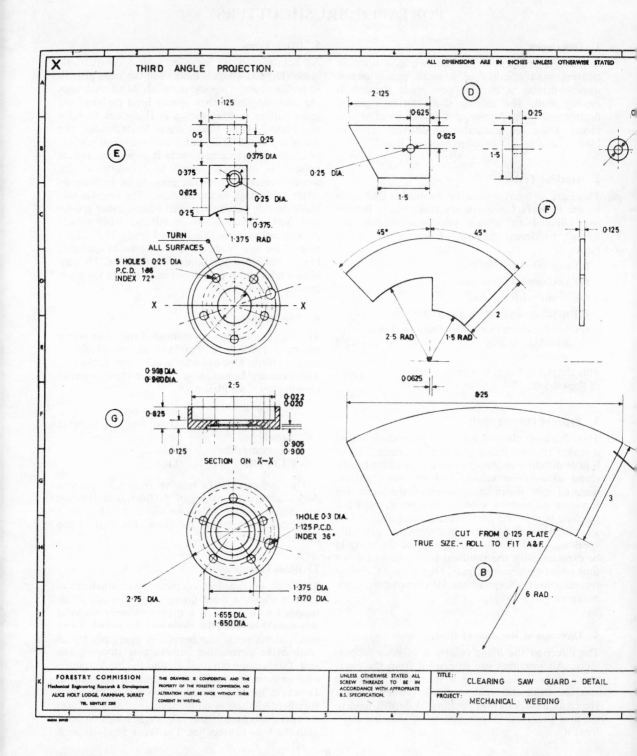

THIRD ANGLE PROJECTION.

ALL DIMENSIONS ARE IN INCHES UNLESS OTHERWISE STATED

TURN ALL SURFACES

5 HOLES 0·25 DIA
P.C.D. 1·88
INDEX 72°

SECTION ON X—X

1 HOLE 0·3 DIA.
1·125 P.C.D.
INDEX 36°

CUT FROM 0·125 PLATE
TRUE SIZE.- ROLL TO FIT A&F.

6 RAD.

FORESTRY COMMISSION
Mechanical Engineering Research & Development
ALICE HOLT LODGE, FARNHAM, SURREY
TEL. BENTLEY 2255

THIS DRAWING IS CONFIDENTIAL AND THE PROPERTY OF THE FORESTRY COMMISSION. NO ALTERATION MUST BE MADE WITHOUT THEIR CONSENT IN WRITING.

UNLESS OTHERWISE STATED ALL SCREW THREADS TO BE IN ACCORDANCE WITH APPROPRIATE B.S. SPECIFICATION.

TITLE: CLEARING   SAW   GUARD — DETAIL

PROJECT: MECHANICAL   WEEDING

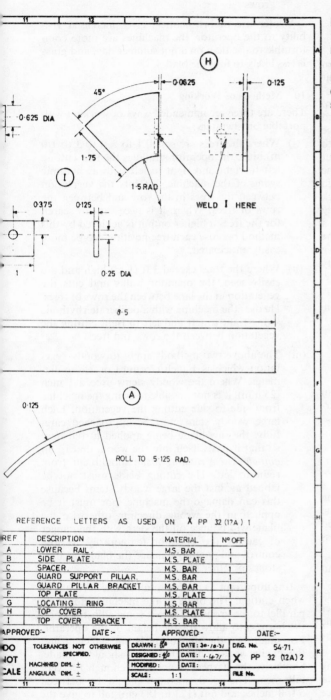

Diagram 10. Plan of a modified guard for a Husqvarna clearing saw

0·0625

0·125

45°

0·625 DIA

H

1·75

1·5 RAD

WELD I HERE

I

0·375   0·125

0·25 DIA

1

8·5

0·125

A

ROLL TO 5·125 RAD.

REFERENCE LETTERS AS USED ON X PP 32 (12A) 1

REF	DESCRIPTION	MATERIAL	N° OFF
A	LOWER RAIL.	M.S. BAR	1
B	SIDE PLATE.	M.S. PLATE	1
C	SPACER.	M.S. BAR	1
D	GUARD SUPPORT PILLAR.	M.S. BAR	1
E	GUARD PILLAR BRACKET	M.S. BAR	1
F	TOP PLATE	M.S. PLATE	1
G	LOCATING RING	M.S. BAR	1
H	TOP COVER	M.S. PLATE	1
I	TOP COVER BRACKET	M.S. BAR	1

APPROVED:-		DATE:-		APPROVED-		DATE:-

DO NOT SCALE	TOLERANCES NOT OTHERWISE SPECIFIED.	DRAWN:	DATE: 30·10·51	DRG. No.	54·71.
		DESIGNED:	DATE: 1·4·71	X	PP 32 (12A) 2
	MACHINED DIM. ±	MODIFIED:	DATE:		
	ANGULAR DIM. ±	SCALE: 1:1		FILE No.	

have devised a guard suitable for the Husqvarna which is shown in Plates 10 and 11. Diagram 10 shows how to make one.

8   Cutting Climbers

Whilst the conventional brushcutter is of value when dealing with woody weeds, the rigidity of their design is a disadvantage where there is a predominance of climbers, especially honeysuckle (*Lonicera periclymenum*) or Traveller's Joy/Old Man's Beard (*Clematis vitalba*) which tend to grow high into the crop trees. Bramble can also be difficult to deal with using a standard machine. In these instances (but because of cost, only where the problem is large) the Wambo brushcutter is of value. The drive is through a flexible shaft from a small engine carried knapsack fashion on the operator's back direct to the cutting head carried on a scythe-like handle suspended by a rubber cord from a hook attached to the top of the knapsack frame (see Plate 12). The flexible drive gives the cutting head considerable manoeuvrability making it easier to deal with climbers and bramble.

Supplier	Description
Turfair Mower Services	Wambo Werker complete
Cranbrook Road Benenden Cranbrook, Kent TN17 4ET	*Price* £145

Spares for the JLO engine can also be obtained from Industrial Power Units Ltd, Vane Street, Wolverhampton, Staffs. WV2 1AD.

9   Recommended Uses of Portable Brushcutters

The main uses of portable brushcutters are:

(i) To cut access into plantations for applying herbicides especially in cutting, say, one lane in 3, 4 or 5 for mistblowing. (A wheeled machine should be used for this work if access is possible.)

(ii) To weed plantations or to remove overhead cover where herbicide treatment is not acceptable because of crop species, amenity considerations, proximity of public water supplies, etc., or where access is unsuitable for wheeled machinery because of the overhead cover or steep slopes.

(iii) Preparation of ground for planting, cutting woody growth from drain sides prior to drain maintenance and clearing along fence lines prior to their being renewed where other machinery cannot be used.

(iv) For cutting woody weeds between trees after a wheeled brushcutter has cut between the rows.

Winter use of brushcutters gives increased visibility to the operator, the machines are more comfortable to use than on a hot summer day, and grass is less likely to foul the blades.

10   Methods of Working

There are three recommended ways of working with portable brushcutters:

(i) Where the trees are small, 1 to 3 ft (0·3 to 1·0 m) high, the operator straddles the row cutting left to right and right to left with a rhythmic swing of the machine. He cuts the vegetation between the trees in the row and between the rows of trees. Where it is necessary to search for the trees a higher output is achieved by this method because each tree position can be more easily anticipated.

(ii) Where the trees exceed 3 ft (1 m) high and are easily seen, the operator walks and cuts the vegetation in the lane between the rows of trees. He uses the machine with a deliberate rhythmic swing right to left and left to right cutting the vegetation between the rows and trees.

(iii) The above two methods apply to woody vegetation which is 1 inch (25 mm) or less in diameter. Where the woody stems exceed 1 inch (25 mm), it is not possible to swing the machine from side to side cutting the vegetation. Each large woody stem must be approached carefully, the saw blade being applied to the stem so that it feeds itself into the wood, that is, an *anti-clockwise rotating blade* should cut from right to left. The cutting blade must not be jabbed against the large woody stems because this can damage the machine, nor must it be applied in the wrong direction otherwise the blade will bounce off the stem with the danger of causing the operator temporarily to lose control and possibly damage the blades against stones or other obstacles.

It is important to maintain full engine revolutions when cutting. The blade of the machine should be parallel to the ground. There is some adjustment on the harness to allow for the height of the operator. For small men the adjustment is not sufficient and the engine is too near the right shoulder blade. Similarly, the harness is not long enough for very tall men. The ideal operator should be between 5 ft 8 inches and 6 ft (173 to 183 cm) tall to give the most comfortable and efficient balance between man and machine.

Plate 1. "There is nothing new under the sun". Men preparing to spray against mildew in 1917.

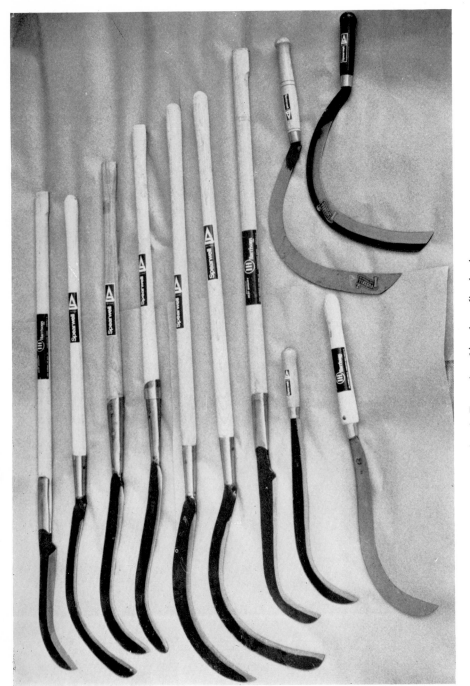

Plate 2. Examples of hand weeding hooks:
From top to bottom:
1. Harrison 785 Light brushing hook
2. Spear and Jackson 4654 Light brushing hook
3. ,, ,, 4607 Heavy ,, ,,
4. ,, ,, 4605 ,, ,, ,,
5. ,, ,, 4651 Light ,, ,,
6. ,, ,, 4655 ,, ,, ,,
7. Harrison 780 ,, ,, ,,
8. Spear & Jackson 4707 Bean hook
9. Harrison 795 ,, ,,
10. Spear & Jackson 4709 Reap hook
11. ,, ,, 4700 ,, ,,

WS 2/96/2

Plate 3. The Dutch Weeding Scythe with cutting head (inset); note coppice hook behind blade.

WS 2/98/22
WS 2/98/24

Plate 4. The 'S' hook developed by the Forestry Commission. *Left:* early design. *Right:* the hook as now used. WS 2/25/9

Plate 5. Tool maintenance equipment – Edge tool gauge, sharpening stone with two different faces and carrying frog. B 6607.

Plate 6. The Husqvarna 65 clearing saw. WS 3/4/4.
Plate 7 (Inset). Alternative grass cutting blade. WS 3/4/1

Plate 8. An example of a close fitting type of guard supplied with some brushcutters. It tends to clog all too easily and can be dangerous.

Plate 9. The guard supplied with the Stihl brushcutter. It is unlikely to clog with cut vegetation. WS 2/21/18

Plate 10. Modified guard made in Work Study Research and Development workshop for the Husqvarna clearing saw. WS 3/7/19

Plate 11. Another view of the modified guard for the Husqvarna clearing saw. WS 3/7/17

Plate 12. The flexible drive Wambo brushcutter with its scythe-like handle and circular saw blade cutting head. NIAE 45280

Plate 13. Mayfield autoscythe with reciprocating blade cutter bar. WS 2/36/19

Plate 14. The Belos tractor fitted with 30″ (76 cm) rotary knife cutter. WS 3/14/13

Plate 15. The Belos tractor showing the cutting head. WS 3/15/15

Plate 16. The guard fitted to the Belos tractor in raised position. WS 3/14/14

11 Protection of the Operator

Portable brushcutter operators should be supplied with the following protective clothing:

(i) A heavy duty PVC apron.

Supplier	Description
James North	North PVC Apron Type
& Sons Ltd.	A 42
P.O. Box 3	Size:
Hyde	Length 42″ (107 cm),
Cheshire	Width 36″ (91 cm)
SK14 1RL	Price 72p

(ii) A pair of leather gauntlet gloves.

Supplier	Description
Industrial Glove	Chrome Leather single
Co. Ltd.	palm inseam gauntlets Type
Nailsea	26E
Somerset	Size
BS19 2BX	Large man's 35 cm (14 in)
	overall length
	Price: 88p

Most brushcutters have a stay from the handlebar to the driveshaft tube, which though its main purpose is to support the handle, also assists the operator to lay the cut vegetation and protects him from thorns.

(iii) Ear defenders.

Supplier	Description
James North	North Auralguard Type
& Sons Ltd.	ED 1702
P.O. Box 3	Headband ear defender
Hyde	Price
Cheshire	£4.00 with reduction for
SK14 1RL	quantity

(iv) Leather boots preferably with safety toe caps.

Noise and Vibration

Trials show that flexible drive machines are generally more acceptable than rigid drive models. As long as the use of a portable brushcutter is not unduly prolonged, operators of any of the well known makes of machine are unlikely to suffer ill effects if the above protective clothing is worn. At the time of writing Messrs Thomas Niven Ltd of Dalston Road, Carlisle, CA2 5NS, announced the new Stihl FS 20 brushcutter, and the Husqvarna Company had introduced the 165R; both have anti-vibration handles. A new generation of lightweight machines is emerging from Japan.

12 Care of the Machine

To ensure machine efficiency the following recommendations are made:

(i) The fuel should be mixed to the maker's recommended ratio, *using two-stroke self-mixing oil*, the fuel can being clearly marked to show its contents.

(ii) Daily cleaning of the air filter is essential.

(iii) A new or clean sparking plug should always be available to the operator.

(iv) A feeler gauge is necessary to set the spark plug gap correctly.

(v) A fuel funnel with filter should be standard equipment.

(vi) A simple crate or box in which the saw can be kept should be provided.

(vii) Up to 10 per cent of non-cutting time can consist of fetching fuel, tools, etc. To obviate this, a small portable crate for spares, fuel, filter funnel, blades, etc, is suggested. (See para 14 and Diagram 11.)

(viii) A daily and weekly maintenance schedule should be tacked inside the lid of the brushcutter box.

(ix) Each machine should be supplied with a copy of the manufacturer's handbook.

13 Machine Maintenance

The following minimum maintenance should be carried out:

Daily

Strip, sharpen and set the saw blade.
Clear dry vegetation from the cutting head, especially where there is a possibility of it working through seals and bearings in the cutting head.
Clean the air filter.
Check the tightness of all nuts and bolts, etc.
Grease or oil the cutting head.
Report all faults and defects which cannot be rectified to the supervisor in charge.

Weekly

In addition to the daily check,
Clean the machine.
Check spark plug gap and reset. If necessary, have plug cleaned by sand blasting or replace plug.
Clean and adjust carburettor.

If in doubt about any fault or excessive noise, stop the machine.

14   Simple Crate for Carrying Brushcutter Fuel, Tools, Blades and Spares

The crate is constructed from hardboard and small pieces of timber and is easily made by forest workers during wet time. It can be stored in the brushcutter box overnight and taken to work site during the day.

Materials Required

Hardboard ⅛ in (3 mm) thick

For sides, 2 pieces 14 in x 5 in (36 cm x 13 cm)
For ends, 2 pieces 10 in x 5 in (25 cm x 13 cm)
For base, 1 piece 14 in x 10 in (36 cm x 25 cm)

Timber

For jointing hardboard, 4 pieces 5 in x ½ in x ½ in (13 cm x 13 mm x 13 mm)
For jointing hardboard, 2 pieces 13 in x ½ in x ½ in (33 cm x 13 mm x 13 mm)
For jointing hardboard, 2 pieces 9 in x ½ in x ½ in (23 cm x 13 mm x 13 mm)

For handle frame, 2 pieces 10½ in x ½ in x 2 in (27 cm x 13 mm x 5 cm)
For handle, 1 piece dowelling 10 in x 1 in diameter (25 cm x 2·5 cm).

Nails and Screws

As required.

For easy recognition, it is suggested that the crate be painted in a bright colour such as yellow. This will also help waterproof it.

The method of construction is shown in Diagram 11.

15   Standard Time Table

A standard time table for weeding with a portable brushcutter is given in Appendix II, page 107. The method of using the table is very similar to that for hand weeding – see Chapter 3.

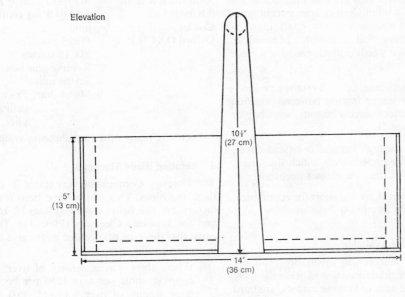

Elevation

10½"
(27 cm)

5"
(13 cm)

14"
(36 cm)

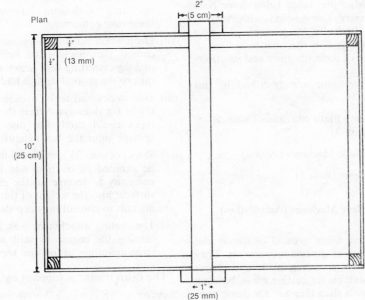

Plan

2"
(5 cm)

½"
(13 mm)

½"

10"
(25 cm)

1"
(25 mm)

Diagram 11. Crate for brushcutter fuel, tools, blades and spares

Chapter 6

PEDESTRIAN CONTROLLED MACHINES

1 General

There are conditions which are still impassable for standard tractors. With modern clearance techniques and wider 7 ft (2·1 m) row spacings, conditions unsuitable for tractors will diminish. Meanwhile, pedestrian controlled weeding machines have a place for weeding in:

(i) narrow row spacings, i.e. 5 ft (1·5 m) or less – but a narrow gauge tractor powered weeding machine is better if access permits, see Chapter 7, para 19, page 21.

(ii) Where there are high stumps, overhead cover, or other similar impediments which the larger, tractor powered machine cannot negotiate.

(iii) Where row lengths are too short for economical working with a tractor powered machine.

2 Types of Machine Available

Machines on the market are invariably built for some purpose other than forestry and generally have too low a clearance and, to varying extents, are hard on the operator. Machines listed below have been used by the Forestry Commission with varying degrees of success. Basically, the principle of a man struggling with this type of machine is not good. Also little is known of their vibration and its effects on the operator.

Three types of machine are described in this chapter:

(a) Reciprocating Blade Machines (Autoscythes) (Para 3)

(b) Rotating Blade Machines (Para 4)

(c) Flail Machines (Para 5).

3 Reciprocating Blade Machines (Autoscythes) (Plate 13)

These machines have a low ground clearance and require a high degree of ground preparation. They cut by means of a reciprocating blade and consequently are more suitable for cutting grass, bracken and herbaceous weeds than they are for dense coppice. Experience has shown that they can become choked with cut vegetation, especially brambles, piling up in front of them and eventually barring their passage. To help overcome this problem, the manufacturers supply a 1 metre long mulch bar.

Supplier of Autoscythes	Description
John Allen & Sons (Oxford) Ltd. Cowley Oxford OX4 3LP	Mayfield tractor fitted with 3 ft (0·9 m) central scythe unit.

Prices

Mk 15 tractor:	£132
Reverse gear box:	£14
Scythe unit:	£49
Mulch bar:	Price on apcation to supplier.

There are many other attachments available.

4 Rotating Blade Machines

The Forestry Commission has tested a number of these machines. Two which have been found satisfactory are the Belos tractor (Plates 14, 15 and 16) and the Wolseley Clearway (Plate 17). Trials indicated that this type of machine might give difficulties in certain conditions:

(i) Where there was a density of over 100 large coppice stools per acre (250 per hectare) and large stumps of over 6 in (15 cms) in height, operating was difficult and manoeuvring around them time consuming.

(ii) Deep wheel ruts and depressions in the ground caused the machine to be thrown around, making operating very heavy work and dangerous, so the ground surface had to be fairly even.

(iii) Side slopes had to be avoided as the machine might tip sideways. When this happened some types could catch fire due to fuel and oil spillage onto the hot exhaust.

(iv) Slopes of over 25% caused difficulty and had to be avoided as traction was lost if it became necessary to reverse up the gradient on a wet surface; also the weight of the machine made it difficult to control on steep slopes.

(v) The cutting attachment was liable to foul up causing the engine to stall where there were large quantities of lop and top.

The Belos tractor is supplied by:

Supplier	Description
Belos Industrial Sales Ltd. Seghill Cramlington Northumberland	Various models are available fitted with 30 in (76 cm) rotary knife mower.
	Price
	About £775

The Belos tractor tested by the Forestry Commission was powered by a 14 h.p. J.L.O. engine which drove the 30 inch (76 cm) horizontally rotating cutting head and the two land wheels through two-speed epicyclic gearing. An instant reverse gear could be operated in both ratios. It is understood that the standard power unit is now (August 1972) the 10 h.p. M.A.G.

The Wolseley Clearway (Plate 17) is also a 30 inch (76 cm) rotating blade type cutter. The height of cut is 1 inch to 5 inches (2·5–13 cm) hence a high standard of ground preparation is required. The Clearway has been modified since it was tested by the Forestry Commission. On the HS model, the 10 h.p. Briggs and Stratton engine drives the wheels through a hydrostatic trans-axle giving infinitely variable speed control and eliminating gear changing. This Wolseley Clearway HS is shown in Plate 17A.

Supplier	*Description*
Wolseley Engineering Ltd.	Wolseley 30 inch Clearway rotary grass cutter.
Electric Avenue	*Price*
Witton	£320
Birmingham B6 7JA	

5 Flail Machines

These machines cut by means of a horizontally rotating shaft carrying a number of vertically rotating flails instead of the horizontally rotating blade of most other pedestrian machines. Flails are of different shapes depending on the vegetation to be cut. These machines are therefore shorter, turn more easily and require less headland for turning purposes. There is an advantage in having flails which rotate in the opposite direction to the ground wheels in that the cut vegetation is lifted from the ground and given a much more effective chop before being finally released at the rear of the flails.

One machine of this type has been tested by the Forestry Commission, the Turner Flailmower (Plates 18 and 19).

Supplier	*Description*
Turner Engineering	Turner 30 inch Flailmower
Co. (Coughton) Ltd.	*Price*
Coughton	£375
Alcester	Twin wheels £16.00 extra.
Warwickshire B49 5QG.	

The machine tested was fitted with heavy duty flails and double wheels. Replacement of broken flails is by means of a simple 'U' clip and requires no spanner. The machine proved to be very stable and not too tiring on the operator.

Chapter 7

TRACTOR POWERED WEEDING MACHINES

1 Types of Machine

Tractor powered weeding machines cut either by means of horizontally rotating chains, horizontally rotating blades, or by vertically rotating flails. A machine may be mounted on the rear or on the front of the tractor, and may be powered from the p.t.o. shaft, by hydraulics, or merely towed (as with rollers). The following systems offer possibilities in forestry and are described in this chapter:

(a) Rear-mounted horizontally rotating chain machines (Paras 9–12)

(b) Rear-mounted horizontally rotating blade machines (Paras 13–21)

(c) Rear-mounted vertically rotating flail machines (Para 22)

(d) Front-mounted horizontally rotating blade machines (Paras 23–28)

(e) Rollers (Paras 29–46).

2 Plantation Layout

Like all modern forestry techniques, mechanical weeding puts a heavy responsibility on the forest manager for planning ahead. It demands a high standard of ground preparation and planting. The requirements may be summarised as follows:

(i) Row lengths should be uninterrupted and as long as possible with planting parallel to drains and rides. A minimum run of 100 metres (say 100 yards) should be aimed at. Costs rise sharply with shorter runs due to the high proportion of turning to cutting time.

(ii) High stumps, large stones, poles and brash from a previous crop will cause damage to the machine or will throw it off course and can also cause tractor bogging. Stumps should be no more than 4 in (10 cm) high and any poles, stones, etc., likely to obstruct, should be removed from the area or laid in the planted row. Reasonable additional expenditure to achieve the higher standard of ground preparation required for machine weeding is justified; the longer the period for which weed control is necessary on any given area, the more justified this additional outlay becomes.

(iii) Planting must be to a high standard with straight rows and accurate spacing between them. There should be at least 6 in (15 cm) clearance between the plants and the tractor wheels. Once a machine is committed to a row, considerable crop damage will occur if the rows converge. At the time of planting, headlands sufficient for the weeding machine to be able to turn without crop damage should be left. With brushcutters, sufficient headland should be left for the machine to swing behind the tractor if weeding is likely to continue after the crop height has reached 3 ft (say 1 m).

(iv) Overhead cover increases mechanical weeding costs by reducing uninterrupted row lengths, particularly when randomly spaced. Where silvicultural or amenity considerations necessitate cover being left, it should where possible be in groups and/or lines, thereby minimising 'broken' weeding rows.

(v) Very severe rutting of the ground at the time of extraction may leave ground conditions which exclude the use, certainly of a pedestrian controlled machine, and possibly some tractor powered equipment. This applies particularly to heavy clay areas and, whenever possible, extraction should be carried out during the drier periods.

(vi) Side slope working is dangerous and must be avoided. Rows should be planted up and down slopes, changing the angle where necessary and leaving appropriate headlands.

(vii) Where the trees are small, chemical spot weeding will be necessary to suppress vegetation which a machine cannot cut immediately around the plants. This operation should be carried out before machine weeding, making the trees visible to the operator.

3 Tractors for Tractor Powered Weeding Machines

Unless otherwise stated, a standard tractor similar to the MF 135 or, in difficult terrain and heavy cutting conditions, the MF 165, is used to power the standard gauge tractor powered weeding machines described in this chapter. It is not considered necessary to print the name and address of suppliers of this easily obtainable equipment.

4 Modifications to the Tractors

Tractors for use with brushcutters should meet the following specifications:

(i) A safety cab must now by law be fitted to all new tractors and is in any event essential with all tractors used on weeding. Where a glass windscreen is fitted, there must also be a windscreen wiper.

(ii) The rear of the cab should be fitted with wire mesh to protect the driver from flying debris.

(iii) The lower parts of the cab need strengthening to protect the operator's legs, tractor foot-pedals, etc., but note that no structural alterations to safety cabs are permissible.

(iv) Metal guarding to radiator, hydraulic pipes, filters, tyre valves, lights, is necessary.

(v) A belly plate must be fitted to give adequate protection and a smooth under surface to the tractor.

(vi) Nylon gaiters should be fitted to all tyres.

(vii) Six-ply tyres are necessary.

(viii) Fixed stabilising bars should be replaced by chains with adjusters.

(ix) A properly dampened seat should be fitted as brushcutting is very hard on the driver.

When a Massey Ferguson 165 or equivalent tractor will be used in more severe conditions, additional modifications are necessary:

(x) A 3:1 low reduction gearbox should be fitted.

(xi) Power steering is strongly advocated.

(xii) The front screen of the cab should be protected by wire mesh.

(xiii) Steel tubes should be fitted from the top of radiator guard to the top front corners of the cab to deflect branches which may otherwise damage the cab and exhaust.

5 Tractor Tools

All tractors should have a full set of the necessary spanners for the particular tractor concerned and should in addition have available on site the following items:

(i) Adjustable spanner

(ii) Pliers

(iii) Screwdrivers (normal and Phillips)

(iv) Block hammer

(v) Oil measure and can

(vi) Funnel

(vii) Grease gun with flexible connector

(viii) Hydraulic jack

(ix) Wheel brace

(x) 3 tyre levers

(xi) Foot pump

(xii) Puncture repair kit

(xiii) Air pressure gauge

(xiv) Winch (e.g. Tirfor)

(xv) Ground anchor

(xvi) Drain crossing bridges

(xvii) Spade

(xviii) Saw.

6 Tractor Power Take Off

The use of a tractor to power a weeding machine in forest conditions is hard work and the usual plastic type of PTO guard supplied for use with agricultural tractors wears rapidly and will soon fail. A metal guard is preferable and will last much longer, hence in a short time costs less. It also has a greater safety factor.

This type of guard can be bought from:

Supplier	Description
Pipe Fabricators (Stamford) Ltd.	Metal PTO guard
	Price
Easton-on-the-Hill Stamford Lincs.	£30–£40

A correctly adjusted torque limiting clutch should always be fitted between the PTO shaft and the machine gearbox. See Para 7 (ii).

7 General Points Relating to the Operation of Brushcutters

Considerable experience has been gained in the best methods of working tractor-powered brushcutters and the main points are as follows:

(i) Damage can be caused to both tractor and brushcutter if the machine comes adrift from the tractor. All linch-pin connections should be replaced by self-locking nuts and bolts.

(ii) A torque-limiting clutch, correctly adjusted to 30–35 lbs per sq inch (200–240 kN/m^2) should be fitted between the PTO shaft and the machine gearbox. (see para 6).

(iii) The PTO shaft and universal couplings should be protected by a metal guard. Plastic guards are not strong enough for forestry work and seldom remain in a safe condition for more than a few hours.

(iv) A sliding bar or chain should replace the top link of the three-point linkage and check chains be fitted to give front end height adjustment, taking the strain from the hydraulic system.

(v) The machine should not be used to cut material beyond its design limits.

(vi) The best cutting height is 6–10 inches (15–25 cm). Unnecessary strain is put on the machine by cutting too low and greatly increases the chances of obstacles being hit.

(vii) Blade machines should be angled so as to run 2 inches (50 mm) lower at the front than the back to avoid the blade recutting the cut vegetation on the back swing. This reduces the power requirements and facilitates self-clearing of the machine by preventing clogging.

(viii) In scrub clearance, the front right-hand side of the tractor should be used to push over the larger vegetation. This allows the blades which are turning anti-clockwise to cut into the back of the stems flattened by the tractor.

8   Brushcutter Maintenance

Because of the heavy strain placed on weeding machines and the vibration, regular maintenance is essential for efficient working:

(i) All nuts and bolts must be checked for tightness twice daily. The use of Loctite or Nylock nuts may help to reduce trouble from this source.

(ii) The gearbox oil level must be checked daily (140 EP oil).

(iii) All greasing points must be attended to daily. (Note: on the Wolseley Swipe Jungle Buster, special attention is necessary to the greasing point for the cutter shaft below the gearbox.)

(iv) The entire machine must be inspected daily for cracks and other damage.

(v) The blades must be sharpened every one or two weeks according to weeding conditions.

REAR MOUNTED HORIZONTALLY ROTATING CHAIN MACHINES

9   General

These machines are rear mounted and the horizontally rotating chains are driven by the tractor power take off. Their use is limited by the chain-type cutting head which restricts them to soft weeds such as grasses, rushes, herbaceous weeds and bracken though they will deal with a season's growth of bramble and light woody weeds providing the latter does not exceed $\frac{1}{2}$ in (13 mm) diameter. Too low a cut should not be attempted in tough matted grass.

10   The Wolseley Swipe

A well tried machine is the Wolseley Swipe Jungle Buster (Plate 20). It gives good reliable service with a minimum of breakdowns. The cutting head consists of a centrally mounted shaft fitted with 3 chains.

It is suitable for weeding in 6 ft (1·8 m) and 7 ft (2·1 m) row spacings or for ride cutting.

Supplier	Description
Wolseley Engineering Ltd.	Wolseley SW 739 Swipe Jungle Buster
Electric Avenue	*Price*
Witton	£280 including cutting
Birmingham B6 7JA	chains.

11   Dimensions

The Swipe gives a 54 in (1·4 m) cut and can be powered by a standard tractor such as a Massey Ferguson MF 135. A version modified by the Forestry Commission for use in 5 ft (1·5 m) row spacing gives a 48 in (1·2 m) cut and can be powered either by a Massey Ferguson MF 135 Vineyard Tractor or by a Holder A 20. Cutting height can be varied from 3 in (8 cm) to 12 in (30 cm) by adjusting the check chains and the rear castor wheel assembly. The Forestry Commission has found it necessary to cut an opening in the rear skirt of the machine (protected by a safety rail) to allow cut vegetation to pass through and hence prevent clogging. Guards consisting of $\frac{3}{4}$ in (20 mm) rubber flaps have been fitted along the front of the machine.

12   Tools and Spares

The following tools and spares should be carried with the machine:

Allen keys, $\frac{3}{4}$ inch AF and $\frac{5}{16}$ inch AF ring spanners.

A spare set of chains and triangles with nuts, bolts and washers.

REAR MOUNTED HORIZONTALLY ROTATING BLADE MACHINES

13   General

These are the sturdiest and most useful of all weeding machines, but, ironically, they have in some areas acquired a bad reputation because the user has expected far too much from them. It must be emphasised that they are primarily weeding machines and designed to cut one year's weed growth of any type of vegetation. If they are used for scrub clearance both the machine and the tractor may be damaged.

14   Standard Gauge Machines

Two machines are used by the Forestry Commission, one made wholly in the USA, the other in Britain but relying on an American gearbox. With both machines, considerable difficulty has been experienced by the importers/manufacturers in obtaining spare parts from the USA.

15   The Bush Hog (Plate 21)

The Bush Hog model 12 is a tractor-powered rotary brushcutter mounted on the tractor hydraulic three-point linkage. The drive is via a 1:1 ratio heavy duty gearbox mounted above the cutters. It is fitted with two free-swinging 22 in (56 cm) heavy duty steel blades, attached to a blade carrying bar, welded to a metal dish. It cuts a 5 ft (1·5 m) swath in a horizontal plane. Height adjustment is from 2–12 in (5–30 cm) and is achieved by means of a fully-castoring adjustable tail wheel assembly. For continuous cutting, 2 in (5 cm) diameter is its maximum cutting ability, with *occasional* stems of up to 4 in (10 cm).

Supplier	Description
Opico (UK) Ltd.	Bush Hog Model 12
47 Westlode Street	*Prices*
Spalding	With Standard blades
Lincs.	£285
	With heavy duty blades
	£295

There are other models.

16   Modifications to the Bush Hog

Maximum working time can be achieved if certain modifications to the machine are carried out before use:

(i) A shoulder should be formed on each side of the gearbox by welding two strips of 6 in x $\frac{3}{4}$ in x $\frac{3}{4}$ in (150 mm x 20 mm x 20 mm) steel to the mounting on either side of the gearbox to prevent the gearbox retaining bolts from shearing.

(ii) The guard and skirt should be strengthened by making continuous welds along all joints and seams.

(iii) The hitch attachment point should be strengthened by welding two 2 in x $\frac{1}{2}$ in (50 mm x 13 mm) metal bars along the length of the machine.

(iv) A steel ring 7 in (180 mm) diameter x 1 in (25 mm) thick should be welded onto the underside of the frame to support the drive shaft from the gearbox.

(v) Two $3\frac{1}{2}$ in x 3 in x $\frac{1}{2}$ in (90 mm x 75 mm x 13 mm) steel bars should be welded across the middle of the dish, on either side and at right angles to the original blade-carrying bar.

(vi) All original welding should be made continuous and metal should be undercut for the new welding.

(vii) A ring of $\frac{1}{2}$ in (13 mm) plate, 6 in (150 mm) inside and 9 in (230 mm) outside diameter should be welded onto the outside of the dish around the centre bolt hole. The edge of the ring should be chamferred and hard faced at the point of contact with the swinging blades.

(viii) A torque-limiting clutch, adjusted to 30–35 lbs/in^2 (200–240 kN/m^2) should be fitted between the PTO shaft and the machine gearbox.

17   The FES Standard Brushcutter (Plates 23 and 24)

This machine is similar to the Bush Hog but of somewhat stouter construction.

Supplier	Description
Farm Equipment Services Ltd.	FES Standard
Spook Hill	Brushcutter
North Holmwood	*Price*
Dorking	£335
Surrey	

18   Output of Standard Gauge Machines

Trials in various conditions have given an indication of likely outputs:

TABLE 3

LIKELY OUTPUTS WITH STANDARD GAUGE REAR MOUNTED ROTATING BLADE BRUSHCUTTERS

Job	Output per day	
	(acres)	(hectares)
A. Ground preparation – Areas where all the vegetation is within cutting ability of the machine.	1–$3\frac{1}{2}$	0·4–1·4
B. Ground preparation – Where a fair proportion of the material is too large for the machine to deal with standing. The brush cutter cuts what it can, providing access for 2 men with a power saw and hooks, returning later to pulverise the cut material.	$\frac{1}{2}$	0·2
C. Ground preparation – As B but a lower proportion of material too large for the machine permitting prior access for 2 men with a chain saw and hook.	$\frac{1}{2}$	0·2
D. Normal weeding (2·1 m row spacing)	$3\frac{1}{2}$–$8\frac{1}{2}$	1·4–3·4

An output guide is *reproduced* in Appendix II, page 126.

19   Narrow Gauge Machines

For use in 5′ (1·5 m) row spacings, a narrow gauge

machine is necessary. The Forestry Commission has built its own narrow gauge machines (see Plates 25 and 26) but one with a fixed cutting width of 4 ft (1·2 m) is now available commercially:

Supplier	Description
Farm Equipment Services, Ltd.	FES Narrow
Spook Hill	gauge brush-
North Holmwood	cutter
Dorking	Price
Surrey	£340

Early work by the Work Study Branch was to produce a variable width machine to cut in 5 ft (1·5 m), 6 ft (1·8 m) and 7 ft (2·1 m) row spacings; in each case the cutting heads were 12 in (30 cm) less than the row spacing to allow 6 in (15 cm) clearance between the sides of the machine and the plants. These machines were however somewhat cumbersome when used at their narrowest setting (for which they were mainly needed) because they had to be long enough to cope with the size of blade required for the widest cut. In practice, the commercially available standard machines are quite satisfactory for 6 ft (1·8 m) and 7 ft (2·1 m) row spacings and the narrow guage machine for the 5 ft (1·5 m) row spacing.

20   Tractors for Narrow Gauge Machines

Tractors suitable for the narrow gauge weeder are the Massey Ferguson MF 135 Vineyard and the narrow Holder tractors.

Supplier of MF 135 (Vineyard)	Description
Holloway, Hinson & Co Ltd.	MF 135 Vineyard Tractor
Oving Road	Price
Chichester	£1632 plus safety cab
Sussex	

Supplier of Holder	Description
Gebrüder Holder	Holder AM2, and AG3
Maschinenfabrik	tractors
7418 Metzingen/Württ	Price
W. Germany	£1120–£1500 at UK port (including import duty).

Note 1.   There was at the time of writing, no agent for Holder tractors in Great Britain, but enquiries can be directed to the following firm:

Chieftain Forge Ltd.
Burnside Road
Bathgate
West Lothian

Note 2.   Holder A 20 tractors used by the Forestry Commission for weeding work have already done a tour of duty on extraction in mountain areas. This particular model is no longer made.

The Massey Ferguson 135 Vineyard tractor has a minimum overall width of 3 ft 9 in (115 cm) when fitted with 9·24 x 5·15 tyres. It has 2-wheel drive. Because of its reduced width, extra care must be taken when working on slopes. The Holders are small 23–34 HP frame steered tractors with four wheel drive. Their minimum width is 30″ (77 cm) and the ground clearance 9¼ in (23·5 cm). They should not work on a side slope of more than 20% (1 in 5).

21   Brushcutter Tools and Spares

The tractor tool kit should serve for normal maintenance but the following additional items are necessary:

1 x 1⅟₁₆ inch AF socket for changing blades

1⅛ inch W Socket for changing dish

¾ inch AF high lift ring spanner for gearbox retaining bolts

18 inch (45 cm) Stillson wrench

¾ inch drive socket bar approx. 22 in (55 cm) long

A torque spanner is necessary for periodic checks on the torque-limiting clutch.

The following spares should be kept with the machine:

1 dish, 2 sets of blades, 2 pivot bolts, nuts, spring washers and keys, 1 dish-retaining nut.

REAR MOUNTED VERTICALLY ROTATING FLAIL MACHINES

22   Description

This type of machine is equipped with rear mounted vertically rotating flails instead of the more usual horizontally rotating cutters. The Forestry Commission uses the Wilder Scrub-Masta '40', a machine designed for forestry. It has two rubber tyred wheels and is usually attached to the 3 point linkage of a tractor being powered through the power take off shaft. The company makes three models, the Scrub-Masta '40' (Plates 27–27A) which cuts a 40 in (1 m) swath, the Mulch-Masta 52 cutting a width of 52 in (1·3 m) and the 6 ft Mulch-Masta cutting a width of 72″ (1·8 m). Height adjustment is from ground level to 10 in (25 cm). The maximum diameter of woody weeds cut should not exceed 2 in (5 cm) for the Mulch-Mastas. The Scrub-Masta '40' is designed to cut up to 4″ (10 cm) diameter material.

Supplier
John Wilder (Engineering), Ltd.,
Wallingford,
Berks.

Description	Price
Heavy Duty mounted Scrub-Masta '40' on 6·50 x 16 x 8 ply tyres (scrub model with block buster flails)	£650
Mulch-Masta 52 trailed machine with cranked flails on 6·50 x 16 x 8 ply tyres	£618
6-foot mounted Mulch-Masta with cranked flails on 18 x 7 x 8 ply tyres	£640

Different flails are available for chopping brash or lop and top. Except for the 6-foot machine on which the wheels can be set behind when required, these machines do not cut to their full width because of their side-mounted wheels.

FRONT MOUNTED HORIZONTALLY ROTATING
BLADE MACHINES

23 General

It had for long been felt that the following advantages should follow from mounting a machine at the front of the tractor instead of behind it:

(i) Better visibility and control for the operator resulting in reduced crop damage and less operator fatigue.

(ii) The machine would cut a path for the tractor thereby increasing tractability and reducing tractor damage.

(iii) Obstacles would be located by the cutter first, thus reducing the chances of "bellying" the tractor on stumps, etc.

This chapter describes the prototype machine built by the Work Study Branch of the Forestry Commission to give these advantages.

24 The Tractor (Plate 28)

The tractor chosen to power the machine was a McCormick International 523, a 48 BHP tractor with hydraulic controls. It was therefore possible to reverse the driving position easily.

25 The Brushcutter (Plates 28 and 29)

The brushcutter is 5 ft 6 in (1·7 m) wide and is attached to the tractor by the 3 point linkage. Guarding of the cutters is by a 12 in (30 cm) deep skirt along the sides, a hinged plate, and heavy rubber flaps to the rear. To the front a heavy hinged metal plate (see Plate 29) extends 12 in (30 cm) ahead of the cutting arc. A hydraulic motor, mounted over the cutting head, powers two free swinging 22 in (57 cm) long heavy duty steel blades attached to a blade carrying bar welded to a metal dish which cuts a 5 ft (1·5 m) swath in a horizontal plane. The cutting head adjustment is from 3 in (7·6 cm) to 30 in (76 cm) by means of the three point linkage hydraulic system. The top linkage incorporates a hydraulic ram which enables the angle of the cutter to be varied from 7° below the horizontal to 20° above.

26 Problems Found During Trials

The following points arose from the field trials:

(i) Because of the modifications to the tractor transmission, the differential lock was no longer available, much reducing the machine's mobility.

(ii) Problems arose with the cooling of the hydraulic oil driving the cutter motor.

(iii) It was difficult to guard the steering track rods adequately.

(iv) The keys which fixed the steering arms to the king pins broke on several occasions.

(v) To give extra lift to the cutter, longer-than-standard hydraulic lift arms were fitted. This, combined with the high weight of the cutter, made the machine front-heavy resulting in problems with the rear wheel steering.

(vi) The tractor transmission system had two faults:

(a) The minimum speed of approximately 1 mph (1·6 km/h) was too fast for heavy cutting.

(b) When used in its lowest range, no braking effect was obtained from the engine because of the free wheel system

(vii) Difficulties of vision were experienced at times by the driver when looking through the front windscreen of the cab (formerly the rear window) which had a reverse angle rake.

(viii) Engine overheating occurred on several occasions because of blockage of the radiator cooling fins. A fine mesh metal radiator grill was fitted which reduced the problem.

27 Output

Job	Output per day	
	(acres)	(hectares)
Cleaning	3·75	1·5
Ground preparation:		
*Site 1	2·0	0·8
Site 2	3·25	1·3
Weeding	4·0	1·6
Chopping lop and top after clear fall	1·75	0·7

Description of Sites

1   Dense hazel coppice 10–16 ft (3–4·5 m) high;
average 10 ft (3 m) between stools; 5–30 stems
per stool, averaging 15; ½–3″ (13–76 mm)
diameter, averaging 2″ (50 mm). Light ground
vegetation of bramble, briar, willow herb, grasses
and rushes. Area flat and dry with no drains.

2   Scrub oak and larch with hazel and sallow coppice. Height 10–16 ft (3–5 m); diameter up to 4″
(100 mm) with the oak and larch, averaging 2″
(50 mm). The other 50% of area consisted of
dense dead grass and bracken forming a mat
6–8″ (150–200 mm) deep. The area was flat and
dry with no drains.

28 Conclusions

(i) For normal weeding, the front mounted brushcutter is too sophisticated and costly and lacks
tractability. Reversing the controls on a normal
two-wheel drive tractor has created problems
when the driving wheels, instead of the steering
wheels, drop into an unseen ditch.

(ii) In heavy weeding/cleaning and ground preparation, its maximum cutting capacity is no greater
than a standard rear-mounted brushcutter. To
increase the capacity, two major modifications
would be necessary:

(a) a larger tractor with four-wheel drive;

(b) a different type of cutting head. Up to now,
horizontally rotating cutters have been considered the most suitable for cutting vegetation. If this method is to continue, a
cutting head incorporating at least four
blades, shorter and rotating at a higher
speed than on present machines will be
required. However, the principle of verti-

cally rotating flails seems a better one. This
type of cutting action is thrown out of
balance far less when obstacles are struck
and does not exert the same high turning
moment on the connections between the
cutter and tractor. Since cut material is
mainly thrown downwards, there is less
danger from flying debris.

(iii) Front mounting of the cutter is an improvement
ergonomically both as regards operator control
and in reducing driver fatigue. With the machine
locating obstacles, delays due to bellying of the
tractor and also tractor damage are reduced. It
was anticipated that its capacity to cut would be
increased by cutting ahead of the tractor. However, as the maximum capacity of the cutters is
no more than the tractor is able to push over
when fitted with a standard rear-mounted
cutter, the anticipated improvement did not
materialise.

(iv) The hydraulic drive system to the cutters has
proved very successful. It eliminates the shock
loading to the tractor transmission system and
has itself been trouble free apart from the overheating already mentioned which can be overcome comparatively easily.

(v) In its present form, it is a single purpose
machine hence sufficient work must be found
for it all the year round. The tractor cannot
easily be uncoupled and used for other work.
A breakdown with either the tractor or the
cutter renders both inoperable.

(vi) Ideally, any future machine of this basic design
would have a greater value as a heavy weeding/
cleaning and ground preparation machine than
from the post planting weeding view point and
should incorporate the following specifications:

(a) More powerful tractor of at least 75 BHP.

(b) Four-wheel drive.

(c) Based on, or built specifically as a forward control tractor, i.e. operator at the
front.

(d) Hydraulic drive to the cutters.

(e) Flail type cutters rotating in a vertical
plane or a faster rotating 4 bladed
horizontal cutter.

(f) Fitted with a winch for debogging.

(g) Overall width to be no more than 6 ft
(1·8 m) to enable it to be used in 7 ft
(2·1 m) row spaced plantations.

ROLLERS

29 General

Cutting weeds with an edge tool may not prevent them from regrowing and requiring several weedings a year. In 1960, certain German foresters*, faced with an annual grass weeding programme of about 3700 acres (1500 ha) in Baden-Württemburg, developed a machine to roll and crush the grass rather than cut it to try to reduce the number of weedings required. The machine they produced, the "Graswalze", looked rather like a motorised garden roller with two rollers set 2½ in (5 cm) apart to allow it to work astride a row of small trees. The power unit was a 2 HP two-stroke engine sitting astride the rollers. This machine, which was pedestrian controlled, is said to have worked reasonably well but was expensive, over £400 at 1972 exchange rates.

A problem weed in Great Britain is *Calamagrostis epigieos*, which, during the wet summer of 1968 was recorded as growing at the rate of 8 in (20 cm) in seven days in the Northampton clay area. Cutting with a blade gave only a temporary respite from its prodigious growth; paraquat had a similar effect to the reap hook. Trials with a tractor-mounted rotary cutter reduced costs but did little to reduce the problem of regrowth until it was noticed that grass crushed by the tractor wheels did not stand up again nor did it grow again for some considerable time. Hence the decision to build a tractor powered grass roller was taken.

30 The Mark I Roller (Plate 30)

The first roller built was very simple. It consisted of a drum 4 ft (1·22 m) wide and 2 ft 6 in (0·76 m) in diameter. Angle iron 1 in x 1 in x ¼ in (25 mm x 25 mm x 6 mm) was welded across the face of the roller at 4 in (100 mm) centres. The roller was attached to the tractor by a Y-shaped yoke and an eye hook. Weight was added by filling the roller with water; 120 gallons (560 litres) of water being required to fill it completely.

The nett weight was 785 lbs (356 kg) and the gross weight 2020 lbs (916 kg). A narrow gauge Massey Ferguson 135 Vineyard tractor was used to tow the roller between 5 ft (1·5 m) spaced rows. The overall width of this tractor is 3 ft 9 in–5 ft 0 in (1·15 m–1·42 m) according to the wheel setting. In wider spacings a standard MF 135 tractor was used.

Control of grass, herbs and bracken with this roller lasted much longer than hand or mechanical cutting. Weeds flattened by the roller during the growing season remained green but lay flat, whereas vegetation cut with a hook or machine rapidly regrew from the base.

31 The Mark II Roller (Plate 31)

The success of the Mk I roller, which was built principally to test the effectiveness of rolling, led to the construction of the MK II model.

Two rollers 3 ft (1 m) wide, each similar to that of the Mk I roller, were towed in line astern behind the tractor and could be moved apart hydraulically so that any width between 3 ft and 6 ft (1 and 2 m) could be rolled. The rollers could also be angled hydraulically so that they would run on the skew and impart a tearing action to the vegetation. When rolling in narrow-spaced plantations, the weed growth was rolled twice by the tandem rollers.

The MK II verson was designed:

(i) to roll between rows of trees planted in rows spaced at 5 to 7 ft (1·5 m to 2·1 m) apart in one pass using the variable width mechanism, and

(ii) to enable the rollers to be run on the skew to tear the vegetation.

This machine functioned well in the flat sandy pine country of Norfolk and Suffolk and in the old woodland areas of Northants and Lincolnshire, but the following disadvantages became apparent during the trials:

(i) The combined weight of the two rollers was too great for the tractor to manoeuvre over old banks, ditches, stumps and other obstacles.

(ii) The roller/tractor combination was too long. It needed a very wide headland, and if it had to leave the row to avoid obstructions, it ran over a considerable number of trees in the adjacent row.

(iii) It could not be taken on to the public road to travel from wood to wood.

(iv) Obtaining water to refill the rollers after transporting the machine was often difficult.

(v) The angle iron cross-bars were damaged by travelling on forest roads.

(vi) It could not be backed successfully.

(vii) Although robustly constructed, running over ditches and stumps exerted considerable stresses, and breakages of the frame were common.

(viii) There was no evidence that the angling of the rollers and the tearing action thereby imparted gave better vegetation control.

---

*See "The Grass Roller, a new weeding principle" by H Weiss and B Wenzler of the Forester Training School, Hinterlagenbach, West Germany. *Allg. Forstzeitschrift* 19(18) 2.5.64 (267–269).

32   The Mark III Roller (Plates 32 and 33)

Some of the problems associated with the MK II roller were in common with the MK I, i.e. neither machine could be taken on to public roads and there was difficulty in obtaining water supplies. In consequence, the machines were unacceptable to field supervisors. A MK III roller was therefore designed to overcome these problems. It has its own undercarriage to enable it to travel on public roads and is now available commercially:

Supplier	*Description*
J H B Implements Ltd.	J H B Weed Control Roll
Ickburgh	(4 ft)
Thetford	*Price*
Norfolk	£248
IP26 5JG	

33   Output

Output is high; in ideal conditions it should be possible to roll more than 10 acres (4 ha) per day but a fair average with an experienced operator in 7 ft (2·1 m) row spacing would be 7·5 acres (3 ha).

34   Organisation of the Job: Plantation Layout

As with all mechanical weeding situations, plantation layout is of paramount importance. To obtain maximum output, obstructions must be reduced to a minimum during preplanting work and the rows set out as long and straight as practical. See also Chapter 7, para 2.

35   Time of Rolling

The best time to roll to obtain maximum effect is just as the weeds have achieved their maximum growth, i.e. usually at flowering. If the trees are small and are likely to be difficult to see, rolling can take place earlier; but it will be slightly less effective. Rolling can be continued as late into the season as desired but the more it is delayed the less will be the benefit to the trees of the freedom from competition during their growing period by earlier weeding.

36   Tree Visibility

Good tree visibility is essential. With small trees it can be achieved by spot weeding with atrazine, paraquat or chlorthiamid earlier in the season.

37   Job Planning

The local supervisor should prepare a job layout which should be made known to the tractor driver. Speed of work is so high that not knowing where to go next can be a major cause of lost time. With an output of 10 acres (4 ha) per day, ½ hour of indecision can loose one acre (about 0·5 ha) output

for that day and increase the cost of the remaining 9 acres (about 3·5 ha) by some 11 per cent. Provided the trees can be seen relatively easily, the driver should re-enter the plantation 2–3 rows ahead of the row he rolled last. This cuts down the turning time and tree losses which can be considerable if he tries to re-enter the next row.

38   Filling the Roller with Water, etc.

A small air space must be left in the roller to allow for expansion in hot weather. If the roller is to be left permanently filled in winter time, antifreeze must be added. It is safer to drain the roller when the season's work is finished. Weed control will be considerably reduced if the water ballast is reduced, but this may be desirable to allow uphill rolling or where ditches have to be crossed.

39   Tools

In addition to the normal tools required for the maintenance of the tractor and roller, a small spade is useful to remove caked mud from the roller ridges and a Tirfor winch should be carried to debog the tractor.

40   Roller Maintenance

Maintenance of the roller is reduced to greasing the bearing and hitch once a day. There is virtually nothing to go wrong or break.

41   Varying the Width of Roll

The width of rolling can be varied by setting the tractor wheels to roll the edge of the strip to be treated. Depending on the size of the tree, at least 6 in (15 cms) should be left at each side of the roller. The Massey Ferguson range of tractors can be set at 4 in (100 mm) variations from 3 ft 9 in (1·15 m) on a Massey Ferguson 135 Vineyard to 7 ft 3 in (2·2 m) on a standard Massey Ferguson 135.

42   Ground Compaction

As the tractor and roller are riding on a mat of vegetation, soil compaction is minimal. No adverse effect, such as a change in vegetation to rushes, was noted on an area which was rolled on three different occasions.

43   Mulching Effect

There are indications that the unpulverised mulch produced by rolling protects the soil from the effects of the wind and sun and reduces weed growth the following season. The flattened vegetation would be unlikely to burn easily.

44 Limitations of Grass Rollers

The grass roller has little effect on light woody growth although brambles and climbers are laid at ground level. If an area is treated with herbicides at the time of planting, woody growth can usually be controlled by an occasional cut with a tractor mounted rotary brushcutter. No trials were conducted on slopes, but obviously the tractor is limited to what it can pull up a forward slope. Cross slopes should not occur if the plantation is correctly laid for machine weeding. (See Chapter 7, para 2.)

45 Tractor for Rolling in Narrow Gauge Plantations

In 5 ft (1·5 m) row spacings, the Forestry Commission uses the Massey Ferguson MF 135 Vineyard tractor as a power unit. For details see Chap 7, para 20. In these circumstances, larger wheels (12·4/11-28) are fitted to give greater ground clearance and better

traction but the overall width is increased to 4 ft 2 in (127 cm). It is likely that one of the narrow Holder tractors would also be suitable.

46 Conclusions

Rolling is the cheapest method yet devised for the control of dense grass, herbaceous weeds and bracken. Very low costs allow rolling to be competitive with other methods even where operating conditions are far from ideal. Capital requirements per acre (or hectare) of plantation in weeding are very low due to the very high output and practically indestructible nature of the machine. Maintenance is minimal and there is no transmission shock to the tractor as occurs in PTO powered weeders. Where terrain and vegetation conditions permit, rolling can perhaps achieve the most significant reduction in weeding costs since the advent of herbicides.

PART D
WEEDING WITH HERBICIDES

Chapter 8

INTRODUCTION TO HERBICIDE PRACTICE

1 Herbicides

Recommendations covering the rates, dilution, time of application and suppliers of the herbicides used in British forestry have been published in Forestry Commission Leaflet No 51 *Chemical Control of Weeds in the Forest.** This Bulletin deals in much greater detail with the other aspects of the job such as methods of application, time taken to do the job, protection of the operator, etc.

Table 5, pp. 30–31, summarises the recommendations for applying herbicides currently used by the Forestry Commission. It includes information more recent than Leaflet 51 and published for Forestry Commission staff in the Entopath Chemical Control Supplement.†

A further useful work of reference is the *Weed Control Handbook*Ø now in its 7th Edition.

2 Diluents: General

Most liquid herbicides can only be used when they have been diluted. The type of herbicide and the method of application jointly determine the diluent used. Table 5 shows the diluent and the rate of dilution. In turn, the diluent dictates to some extent the design of equipment. 100% 2,4,5-T is usually diluted with paraffin which will dissolve the galvanisation of storage tanks whereas water will rust ungalvanised tanks. Paraffin can also cause certain types of washers to swell with the result that sprayers seize up. Neoprene washers overcome this problem.

With medium to high volume application of liquid herbicides, organisation of diluent supplies requires considerable care if costs are to be kept within bounds. The problem can be looked at separately for paraffin and for water.

3 Paraffin as a Diluent

Premium grade paraffin (B.S. 2869 Class C1) is used by the Forestry Commission. The cheapest way to buy it is in bulk deliveries of at least 500 gallons (2273 litres). Delivery of paraffin in or into 45 gallon (205 litre) drums can considerably increase the price. The following table shows the premia payable for different sized loads:

TABLE 6

PRICE PREMIA FOR PARAFFIN DELIVERIES

Product	Size of Load		Premium per gallon
	(gals)	approx. metric equivalent in litres	
Premium grade paraffin	40 gal drums 100–199 200–499 500 and over	205 litre drums 451–905 906–2268 2273 and over	5.00p 0·52p Nil 0·42p (concession)

It is therefore well worth installing a 600 gallon (2728 litre) tank at the depot if a minimum of 2500 gallons (11365 litres) is to be used, because the saving from purchasing this quantity at bulk rates will more than pay for the installation of a tank. Most of the major oil companies' distributors will supply a 600 gallon (2728 litre) *ungalvanised* tank (complete with sight gauge, draw-off valve and drain (sludge valve)) at a cost of about £40. The usual dimensions of such a tank are 6′ 6″ x 4′ x 4′ (2 m x 1·22 m x 1·22 m) and the displacement is about 300 lb per square foot (1465 kg per sq m), hence a fairly substantial staging is necessary. Such a staging can be easily made locally from old railway sleepers or butt lengths for about £15, giving a total cost for the tank and staging of £50–£60. The staging should be sufficiently high for gravity feed into the transporting vehicle (Plate 34). 600 gallons (2728 litres) of paraffin is sufficient to spray 12 acres (4·85 hectares) at the rate of 50 gallons per acre (560 litres per hectare). This would last a two-man team, using knapsack sprayers, 4–6 days.

---

*Forestry Commission: Leaflet Number 51. *Chemical Control of Weeds in the Forest* by J. R. Aldhous 1969 HMSO (under revision as F.C. Booklet 43).
†Copies are available free of charge from: Forestry Commission, Forest Research Station, Alice Holt Lodge, Wrecclesham, Farnham, Surrey.
ØJ Fryer and R Makepiece, Blackwell Scientific Publications, Oxford, 1973.

4 Water as a Diluent

The most suitable source of water is the mains supply because it is clean and does not require filtering. The attitude of Water Boards differs considerably on the method of supply which they are prepared to permit. If there is a mains hydrant close to the forest, some Boards are prepared to allow it to be tapped and will supply a key and standpipe at an annual rental of £1. Others are prepared to provide a hydrant at a convenient location for approximately £16. It may be practicable to run a pipe in from the road to the forest depot. Different circumstances will warrant different action but there is everything to be gained by approaching the local Water Board.

Mains water supplies may contain substances such as lime or chalk which can corrode metal spray nozzles thus altering the size of the aperture. Other constituents have been known to erode the nozzles. Nozzles should therefore be checked from time to time. They should not be cleaned with a pin or other hard object; a soft brush should be used. Worn nozzles should be discarded. It should be noted that whilst paraffin should not be stored in galvanised containers, such a container is desirable for water to prevent rust.

Other sources of supply are wells, streams, ponds, etc., but water from these sources should be carefully filtered to prevent the jets clogging. The restrictions of the Water Resources Act, 1963, must also be taken into consideration. Under this Act, which does not apply in Scotland, a water resource/source of supply excludes any lake, pond or reservoir which does not discharge into any other inland water. But if more than 1000 gallons (4546 litres) is removed *AT ANY ONE TIME* from a water resource/source of supply, a licence from the appropriate drainage authority may be necessary. There is some difference of opinion as to the correct interpretation of the words *AT ANY ONE TIME*. The Great Ouse River Board interpret the meaning as 'Per Annum'. If in doubt, consult the appropriate river authority.

5 Methods of Application

The main methods of applying herbicides currently available are as follows:

(a) *Apparatus carried by the operator:*

  (i) Knapsack sprayers – for medium/high volume application of liquids

  (ii) gravity fed sprayers for medium/high volume application

  (iii) motorised knapsack mistblowers for low volume application of liquids

  (iv) ultra low volume applicators – for very small volumes of liquids

  (v) motorised granual applicators – for applying granular herbicides

  (vi) tree injectors – for applying neat or nearly neat herbicides.

(b) *Machine-powered equipment*

  (i) live reel sprayers

  (ii) tractor mounted medium to high volume apparatus

  (iii) tractor mounted mistblowers

  (iv) tractor mounted ultra low volume apparatus (trial stage only)

  (v) tractor mounted granule applicators.

(c) *Aerial application:* (Aerial application is not currently used by the Forestry Commission)

  (i) medium volume application

  (ii) ultra low volume application.

The situation in which these techniques can be used is shown in Table 5.

Protective clothing is necessary for the operators of this equipment, see Chapter 19.

In the above list, the volumes of application can be assumed to be as shown in Table 7.

TABLE 7

VOLUMES OF HERBICIDE APPLIED

Application	Gallons per acre	Litres per hectare
High volume	Over 60	Over 700
Medium volume	25 – 60	300 – 700
Low volume	8 – 15	90 – 175
Ultra low volume	Under 2	5 – 20

6 Output Guides

Output guides for the following herbicide spraying techniques are reproduced in Appendix II, page 95.

Output Guides

TABLE 5   GUIDE TO THE USE OF HERBICIDES IN FORESTRY

(**Pre-planting on left**)

GUIDE TO USE OF

TREATMENT	CHEMICAL	METHOD OF APPLICATION	PRE – PLANTING TREATMENTS												RATE OF DILUTION	
			MAY	JUNE	JULY	AUG	SEPT	OCT	NOV	DEC	JAN	FEB	MAR	APRIL	IMPERIAL	METRIC
cut stump basal bark and frill girdle	100% 2,4,5 – T in paraffin	P H K T	spray only when dry — bark must be saturated to run off								spray a month before planting if possible				12–16 pts per 100 galls paraffin (1)	1·5–2·0 litres per 100 litres paraffin (1)
Tree Injection	50% 2,4,5 – T Undiluted	T I													1 ml at 3 ins centres (2 ins for resistant species)	1 ml at 75 mm centres (50mm for resistant species)
Tree Injection	50% 2,4 – D Aminé Undiluted	T I													1 ml at 3 ins centres (2 ins for resistant species)	1 ml at 75mm centres (50mm for resistant species)
cut stump or trill for resistant species	(5) A.M.S. (ammonium sulphamate)	dry crystals or plastic can and rose or brush	apply to freshly cut stumps								up to 12 weeks before planting				dry crystal rates 4 lb per gall of water	0·4 kg per litre of water
foliage	50% 2,4,5 – T	(4) AS ✳ M ✳ P H T B K					gorse & broom can be killed in winter								5 pts in 30–60 galls of water per treated acre	7 litres in 350–700 litres of water per treated hectare
heather	2,4 – D	(4) AS ✳ M ✳ P H T B K													6–8 pts in 40–60 galls of water per treated acre	8–12 litres in 456–700 litres of water per treated hectare
grasses	dalapon	M ✳ T B P H K	not immediately before or after rain								up to 3 weeks before planting				15 lbs in 30–60 galls of water per treated acre	17 kg in 350–700 litres of water per treated hectare
grasses & herbs	paraquat (gramoxone)	T B P H K	molinia only								up to 3 days before planting				6–8 pts in 30–60 galls of water per treated acre	9–12 litres in 350–700 litres of water per treated hectare
grasses & herbs	Chlor- thiamid (prefix) Dichlo- benil (Casoron 'G')	G D													40–75 lbs of granules per treated acre	45–90 kg of granules per treated hectare
grasses	atrazine	K	not tested in preplanting conditions												6–8 lbs 50% wettable powder in 30–60 galls of water per treated acre	7–9 kg 50% wettable powder in 350–700 litres of water per treated hectare
bracken	dicamba	K M ✳	leave 3–4 months in summer & 4–6 months in winter before planting												6–8 pts in 30–50 galls of water per treated acre	8–11 litres in 350–550 litres of water per treated hectare

FULL WIDTH OF SHADING INDICATES TIME OF APPLICATION GIVING A COMBINATION OF BEST KILL & GREATEST SUITABILITY

NOTES

1. chemical mixture must be agitated frequently: 16–21 pts (100% 2,4,5–T) to 100 galls of paraffin has given satisfactory kill on resistant species (2·0 – 2·6 litres per 100 litres)

2. ✳ with mistblower or aerial spray use the same amount of concentrate diluted in only 8 – 15 galls of water per acre (100 – 175 litres per hectare)

3. summer treatment (with 100% 2,4,5 – T in paraffin) requires care to avoid spraying onto plants or damage to plants from volatilization at high temperatures

4. at present (Jan. 1972) aerial spraying has been suspended by the F.C.

5. see page 44 of Entopath News Chemical Control Supplement for treatment of rhododendron

(Post-planting on right)

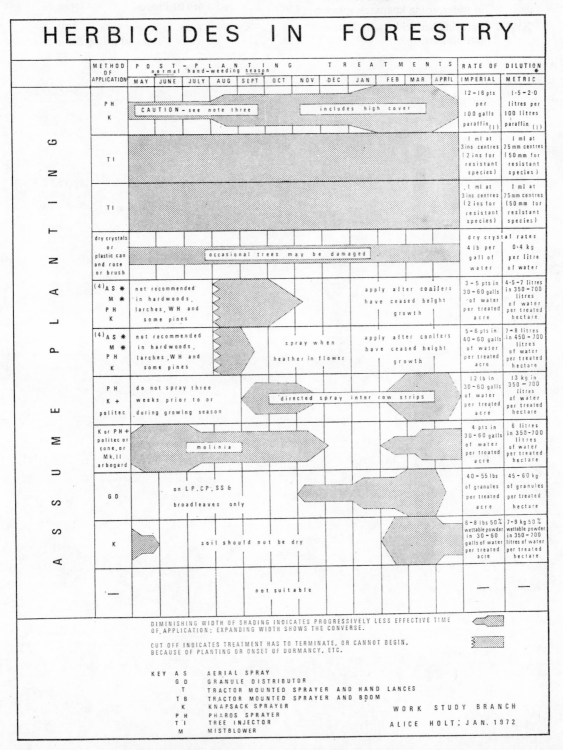

Chapter 9

KNAPSACK SPRAYERS: HAND OPERATED

1 Design

Essentially medium to high volume applicators, these machines fall into two categories:

Compression Knapsack Sprayer

This type of machine must be pre-pressurised to approximately 80 lbs psi (5·6 kg/cm²) before spraying commences. This can be time consuming where large quantities of chemical are to be applied. The container must be robust, usually made of metal, and requires regular safety checks. The weight of the container limits the quantity of chemical carried, and for herbicide application, a pressure control valve is advisable.

Continuously Pumped Knapsack Sprayer

Preferable for forestry use because of its lighter weight and greater capacity, this type of machine incorporates a diaphragm/piston pump and an internal compression cylinder to eliminate any pump fluctuation and ensure an even, continuous output. Liquid is poured into the machine through the filler opening and then pumped through the compression cylinder to the trigger control. A considerable time saving is achieved by pumping whilst spraying is in progress and, because of the lighter weight of the machine, the ability to carry at least 4 gallons (18 litres) of herbicide from any one filling. This type of sprayer is recommended for the application of herbicides in the forest. (See Plates 35 and 36).

2 British Standards

The following British Standards apply to knapsack sprayers and nozzles:

BS 4115 Part 1	1967	Compression Knapsack Sprayers Part 1 Non-pressure-retaining type
BS 4115 Part 2	1967	Compression Knapsack Sprayers Part 2 Pressure retaining type
BS 2968	1958	Hydraulic Spray Nozzles for insect, fungus and weed control.

3 Uses of Knapsack Sprayers

The main uses of a knapsack sprayer in forest weeding are:

(a) To apply herbicides, such as 100% 2,4,5-T in paraffin, to cut stumps and basal bark.

(b) To apply herbicides, such as 50% 2,4,5-T in water, to foliage (a mistblower is a preferable method – see Chapters 11 and 14).

(c) To apply herbicides, such as atrazine in water, to grass or 24-D in water to heather where the tree does not need protecting.

(d) To apply herbicides, such as paraquat in water, to grass around the base of a tree where the tree itself must be protected from herbicide.

(e) Miscellaneous uses, such as inter-row weeding using a dribble bar.

4 The Knapsack Sprayer

An example of a knapsack sprayer employed by the Forestry Commission is the Cooper Pegler C.P.3.

Supplier	Description
Cooper, Pegler & Co. Ltd,	C.P.3 Forestry Model
P.O. Box 9–151	Price
Burgess Hill	£15.85
Sussex RH15 9LA	

The sprayer is equipped with instantaneous trigger control and lance (overall length 28″–71 cm) and No. 520 Nozzle. An extension piece is available to carry a pressure control valve. Whilst the lance has provision for fitting a pressure gauge, this is normally blanked and the gauge must be ordered separately. Other accessories are available and these are mentioned under specific treatments below.

5 Drift and Pressure Control

With any form of sprayer there is always a likelihood of drift. Ideally all herbicides should be applied just to the target area, but in practice most sprayers produce a wide range of droplets, finer droplets being wind carried and causing damage outside the target area. Generally the lower the pressure the larger the droplet and the less chance of accidental damage. It is desirable therefore to fit a pressure control valve to the outlet of the container and a pressure gauge between the trigger control and the lance. The control valve should be set to 4–6 lbs psi (0·28–0·42 kg/cm²). Ideally adjustments should be made with the sprayer on the operator's back and using water, not herbicide. While spraying, the gauge can be removed, to eliminate the possibility of damage, and the socket plug replaced in the lance. One gauge only is required for setting up to 5 machines.

6 Application of Herbicides where the Tree Does Not Need Protecting

Such application includes, *inter alia*, basal bark or

cut stump treatment of unwanted woody vegetation using 100% 2,4,5-T diluted with paraffin, foliar spraying with 50% 2,4,5-T in water, spraying atrazine on to grass with the herbicide in suspension in water and spraying 24-D ester in water on to heather. For all these cases the basic equipment is a continuously pumped knapsack sprayer with pressure control valve, pressure gauge as required and standard 28″ (71 cm) lance. The nozzle required for cut stump and basal bark treatment is the No. 520 Rose nozzle. This nozzle is similar to the standard No. 520 but without the swirl core and with a 5-hole (5 x ·040″) solid stream disc, known as a "rose jet". The other treatments require wide angle nozzles, such as the PP.78 floodjet, Polijet or Politip. (Colour plate 3 shows these nozzles; see central inset.)

7 Application of Herbicide Where the Tree Must Be Protected

Paraquat and dalapon should not be sprayed on to trees. To prevent this, a 'U' shaped guard, the Politec, has been designed for use with knapsack sprayers:

Supplier	Description
Cooper, Pegler & Co. Ltd,	Politec guard
P.O. Box 9–151	Price
Burgess Hill	£7.85
Sussex RH15 9LA	

The Politec (Plate 37) screws on to the trigger control in place of the standard lance. The sprayer should be fitted with a pressure control valve, a gauge being used to set the required pressure.

With the Politec, the operator walks between the rows, a right-handed operator spraying trees on his left and vice-versa. The 'U' shaped portion of the guard is placed as close to the base of the tree as possible at about 30° to the row (see Diagram 12). The trigger is then operated to give a two-second burst of herbicide: simultaneously the Politec is revolved through 150°. The object is to apply 42 cc's of herbicide to the square yard around the tree. The Politec is fitted with 2 No. 15 jets, one on either side of the guard and the pressure control valve set at 4–6 lbs psi (0·28–0·42 kg/cm²). It is strongly advised that a calibration run, using water, is made. The diameter of the spray pattern with this attachment can be adjusted in two ways:

(a) By raising or lowering the nozzle fixing brackets in the holes available for this purpose.

(b) By altering the angle of the brackets.

Note: It will be necessary to apply more herbicide if the sprayed area is increased.

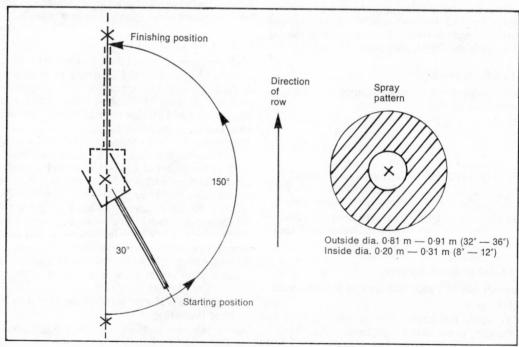

Diagram 12. The Politec—method of use and spray pattern

Periodically the operator must re-charge the compression cylinder of a continuously pumped knapsack sprayer; one fill is sufficient for 10–12 trees.

With the Politec the tree is contained within the guard whilst surrounding vegetation is sprayed. There are alternatives:

(1) Herbicide can be applied without a guard.
(2) The nozzle and not the tree can be contained in a guard.

The first alternative is not recommended except when applying atrazine (see para 8). With both paraquat and dalapon, practice shows that too high a rate of tree mortality can ensue.

The second alternative is useful where it is necessary to spray a larger area than the 4-foot diameter (120 cm) attainable with the Politec. Spray shields (see Plate 38) are available in 3 sizes, 12″ (30 cm) 15″ (38 cm) and 18″ (46 cm) which are supplied complete with nozzles and will fit on to the standard 28″ (71 cm), 21″ (53 cm) and 14″ (36 cm) lances respectively.

Supplier	*Description and Prices*	
Cooper, Pegler & Co.	12″ Spray Shield	£1.85
Ltd,	15″ Spray Shield	£1.92
P.O. Box 9–151	18″ Spray Shield	£2.48
Burgess Hill,		
Sussex RH15 9LA		

It is however both simple and cheap to make up spray shields locally, the easiest method being to use a Politec lance fitted with an inverted washing-up bowl. See Plate 39.

Plate 40 shows another locally-made device using a 1 gallon Gramoxone container with one side cut off, and and a 21″ (53 cm) lance fitted.

8   Application of Atrazine

Atrazine is a relatively new herbicide in forestry for the control of certain grasses. It is recommended for use as a wettable powder and therefore requires rather different mixing and storing techniques than paraquat or dalapon. As a herbicide, its attraction lies in the fact that coniferous trees do not need to be protected from the spray and hence complicated guards are not necessary. Trials of atrazine in its granular form are in progress.

Mixing

The recommended dose rate is 6–8 lbs of atrazine in 30–60 gallons of water per treated acre (7–9 kg in 350–700 litres per treated hectare). The quantity required for a sprayer full (4 galls–18 litres) at 9 kg is circa 360 grammes (13 oz.). A scoop designed to

hold precisely the required weight of powder for a sprayer full is a convenient measuring method. The mixing must be done at the time of filling because if mixed in bulk at a base, the powder, which is merely suspended throughout the diluent, settles out.

The Sprayer

The best means of applying atrazine at present is the continuously pumped knapsack sprayer (see 1 (b)) fitted with a red Polijet or Politip (Colour plate 3).

Method

The following method of working has been developed:

(a) Take sprayer off back
(b) Remove lid
(c) Run some water into the sprayer (to aid mixing)
(d) Run ½ a litre or so into a bucket
(e) Measure the powder into the bucket and stir until thoroughly mixed
(f) Pour this slurry into the sprayer, swill out bucket into the sprayer
(g) Fill sprayer
(h) Screw on lid and wipe sprayer if necessary
(i) Lift sprayer on to stand and load on to back
(j) Walk to site pumping up pressure
(k) Spray over row of trees maintaining walking speed and band width (1 metre) and pressure

Note: Treating square-metre plots has been tested as an alternative to spraying a 1 m strip but is only recommended in ideal conditions. Where trees are small and difficult to locate, the loss of time searching for them will cost more than the saving of chemical.

(l) Mark end of spraying pattern
(m) Return to base and repeat process.

Calibration

In order to achieve the application rate above, the variables which affect the quantity of herbicide applied must be controlled. They are:

(*i*) *Mix*. As stated above, this is 9 kg of atrazine powder in 450 litres of water per *treated* hectare.

(*ii*) *Walking Speed*. A comfortable walking speed over forest ground is 2 mph (3·22 km/h) equivalent to approximately 1 yard a second and is acceptable over all but the very easiest terrain or the steeper slopes.

(*iii*) *Spray Width*. A spray width of 1 metre (achieved when the nozzle is held 25 cm (10″) above ground level) gives adequate control except in areas of very tall vegetation (which in any case are unlikely to be suitable for atrazine) or with very small trees.

(*iv*) *Nozzle*. A red polijet or politip gives an even flow of liquid over the whole band width.

(*v*) *Spraying Pressure*. With these variables fixed, the pressure can then be calculated to give the desired flow. At 3.22 km/h (2 mph) an operator will walk 3220 lineal metres in one hour. If spraying a band 1 metre wide, the spray will cover an area of 3220 sq m in a gross hectare of 10,000 sq m. With the quantity of spraying liquid fixed at say 450 litres per hectare, the spray will need to deliver

$$\frac{3220}{10000} \times 450 = \text{145 litres per hour or one sprayer full of 18 litres in } 7\tfrac{1}{2} \text{ minutes.}$$

With the sprayer on the operator's back and with him maintaining his normal pumping pressure, the pressure control valve will need to be adjusted to give this flow. This can be measured precisely over a litre or two and checked over a sprayer load. The pressure gauge will read between 12–16 pounds per square inch (0·8 and 1·1 kg/cm²) depending on the gauge but the rate of flow must be the criterion (i.e. 1 litre in 25 secs) rather than gauge pressure. Other rates of flow can be calculated for other specifications, e.g.

700 litres per hectare
1·2 m wide band
3 mph walking.

9   Gravity-fed Knapsack Sprayers

With this method of application the diluted herbicide is carried on the operator's back in a 4-gallon (18 litre) container and is allowed to flow by gravity through a tap and some form of distributor on to the weed growth. The cheapest distributor is a T-shaped "dribble" bar. Whilst the dribble bar is available commercially, it is expensive. A cheap and very effective home made version is shown in Plates 41 and 42. It is made from a length of plastic tube which is fed from a four-gallon (18 litre) container fitted with a tap. At the other end, the tube is fixed to a broomstick by adhesive tape and fed into a Geeco number 148 weed killer attachment (a 20″ (51 cm) bribble bar). An on/off device is fitted into the plastic tube by breaking it and slotting in a 2″ (5 cm) length of rubber tube at a convenient point. Pressure of the thumb will halt the flow of herbicide as required.

Supplier	Description
G and E Equipment and Contracts Ltd Geeco Works New Milton Hants. BH25 6SE	Number 148 weed killer attachment *Price* 32p

This attachment is also available from most branches of Boots Chemists. This dribble bar is very useful for interrow spraying and also for strip spraying of herbicides which will not damage the crop trees.

A more complex and expensive sprayer of this type has a small pump which is designed to apply a measured dose of herbicide every time the control lever is operated and has a guard fitted to protect the tree.

10   Application of Ammonium Sulphamate (AMS)

Application studies with this herbicide have not so far been undertaken by the Forestry Commission Work Study Branch because 2,4,5-T is a much easier chemical to use. AMS is highly corrosive when used with copper, brass or steel. The addition of sodium benzoate gives a fair degree of protection from corrosion of brass but not with steel or copper. The best method of application is therefore to use an all plastic watering can with a fine rose or a paint brush and a plastic bucket.

Chapter 10

TREE INJECTORS

1 Introductory

There are a number of machines on the market which are designed to inject herbicides into the tissues of unwanted scrub trees or coppice regrowth of a suitable size. The currently recommended dose rate is one millilitre per cut of a mixture of equal quantities of 100% 2,4,5-T ester and paraffin oil. Cuts should be spaced so that their *centres* are 3" (75 mm) apart on susceptible species such as birch and 2" (50 mm) apart on moderately resistant species such as hazel and oak. The injection should ensure that the herbicide reaches the outer sapwood. As an alternative herbicide, undiluted 2,4-D Amine (containing 5 lbs of acid per gallon) can be used. The treatment is not at present recommended for resistant species such as ash and hawthorn.

2 The Jim Gem

Commercially available machines include the American Jim Gem (Plate Number 43) which is basically a 4-foot (1·2 m) length of metal tube which holds the herbicide, at one end of which is a chisel bit for making a cut into the tree; a lever operates a pump which can inject 1 ml of the herbicide down the chisel bit and into the cut. The cost is approximately £20.

3 The Tree Ject

A similar machine which injects the herbicide automatically each time it is jabbed at the tree, is called the Tree Ject. It too comes from America and costs about £15.

4 The Hypo Hatchet

A third American machine is the Hypo Hatchet which resembles a small boy scout hatchet, the handle and head of which are bored to allow herbicide to be fed in from a reservoir worn on a belt around the waist. When the hatchet hits the tree, a 1 ml dose of herbicide is injected. This machine costs about £40.

5 The Fickningsspruta (or Swedish Water Pistol)

The most successful (and the cheapest) machine is a small repeating water pistol-like device imported from Sweden and known there as the "Fickningsspruta" ("notching sprayer"). This sprayer is used in conjunction with a 1 gallon (4½ litre) container worn over the shoulder and a small boy scout hatchet. The equipment is available as follows:

Suppliers	Description
Fickningsspruta	Injector
Skogsmateriel AB	Type 1662–1 *without*
P.O. Box 12–199	container.
S.102–25 Stockholm 12	*Price*
Sweden	About 50p
Container	*Type*
Cooper Pegler and Co Ltd	1 gallon plastic container with shoulder strap.
P.O. Box 9–151	*Price*
Burgess Hill	80p
Sussex RH15 9LA	
Hatchet	*Type*
Spear & Jackson	3101
(Tools) Ltd	*Price*
St Pauls Road	£1.85
Wednesbury	
Staffs	

A small amount of work is necessary to drill out the hole in the sprayer to $\frac{1}{16}$" and also to drill a hole of suitable size in the cap of the plastic container and fit a grommet to take the sprayer tube.

This apparatus is illustrated in Plate 44.

Chapter 11

MOTORISED KNAPSACK MISTBLOWERS

1 Description

These machines are low volume applicators and are of especial value when applying 2,4,5-T diluted with water to foliage and 24-D in water to heather. Essentially they consist of a container for holding the diluted herbicide, which is fed into the air stream of a fan powered by a small petrol engine. They produce a range of droplet sizes including fine mist which is prone to drift; care is therefore necessary. The Forestry Commission has tested a number of machines among them the following:

Suppliers	Type
(i) Thomas Niven Ltd	Stihl SG 17 knapsack
Dalston Road	mistblower
Carlisle	(See Plate 45)
Cumberland CA2 5NS	Price complete
	£65

This is a lightweight machine weighing 18¼ lbs (8·3 kg) empty and has a capacity of 3·2 gallons (14·5 litres). It has a horizontal fan (unlike most other machines which have vertical fans) and is therefore very stable. A conversion kit to convert the SG 17 mistblower for the application of granules costs £1.62. (See Chapter 12, para 3.)

(ii) Turfair	Type
Mower Services	Wambo WI70
Cranbrook Rd.	Price
Benenden	£49
Cranbrook	
Kent	
TN17 4ET	

A slightly heavier machine weighing 26 lbs (12 kg) empty which has a tank capacity of 3 gallons (13 litres). It has a vertical fan.

The power unit is the JLO L35 2·5 h.p. two-stroke engine. Spares are readily available from the suppliers and also from Industrial Power Units Limited, Vane Street, Wolverhampton, Staffs, WV2 1AD.

2 Time of Application

Mechanical realiability of the machine and efficient working methods are most important because the spraying seasons are short. When mistblowing foliage in planted crops, the last two weeks in August and the month of September are most suitable though some control can be achieved in October and perhaps early November depending on the leaf-fall. With heather control by mistblower (or

U.L.V.), the latitude is a bit better though rather more complex being dependent on tree species, and part of the country, viz:

Tree Species	Northern Britain*	Southern Britain*
Spruce and spruce/pine mixtures	mid July to early September	early August to mid September
Other Species	early August to early September	mid August to mid September

Work on heather control by mistblower was still in progress when this Bulletin was written, hence the remainder of this chapter is based on experience with the application of 2,4,5-T in water to foliage.

*Note Northern Britain is that part of Britain lying north of a line from the Mersey to the Humber.

3 Calibration

Before spraying, calibration runs should always be carried out using water only, remembering that the better the ground conditions, the faster and more easily an operator can walk, and therefore a greater rate of delivery can be used. Putting this another way, the size of the nozzle can be related to the walking speed of the operator – the faster he walks, the greater the mistblower output should be. Another reason for calibration runs is that once the nozzle size and hence the output has been determined, the area that can be sprayed from one tankful is apparent and the number of racks required for access of bulk diluent in 45-gallon (205 litre) drums, semi-rotary pump, hose line, etc., can be calculated.

4 Cutting Racks

When ground conditions permit, racks should be cut by machinery, using such machines as the Bush Hog, Wilder-Rainthorpe Multi-Masta, Wolseley Swipe or a pedestrian controlled machine (see Chapters 6 and 7). If ground conditions are not suitable for these machines, consideration should be given to clearing by means of a portable brushcutter (see Chapter 5). Hand clearing should only be carried out as a last resort.

The distance apart of the racks will depend upon the range of the mistblower, and since most of these machines have fairly short ranges varying from 12–30 ft (3·7 m–9·1 m), a good average distance would be 25 ft (7·6 m). Range is not the only consideration, penetration is also important and if the foliage of the vegetation being sprayed is very thick, it is better to space the racks less than 25 ft (7·6 m) apart, but certainly never more than 25 ft (7·6 m) apart.

5 Cross Racks

If the vegetation is very dense, it may be necessary to put in communication racks at right angles to the rows and to have the distance between them equivalent to the distance that can be sprayed by half a tankful of herbicide. Normally, however, it will be possible for the operator to walk from rack to rack without undue difficulty. Since the cardinal rule of this type of job is to keep walking to a minimum, the diluent supply, whether in drums or pumped from a trailer/tank by means of a semi-rotary pump, should always be sited so that the operator has no more than 30 yds (say 30 m) to walk to refill his container. This means therefore that 45-gallon (205 litre) drums and the pump and stand must be carefully sited, if this method is used.

6 Marking Spraying Area

To mark the extremities of the area that can be sprayed by one tankful, binder twine can be used at right angles to the rows. By this means, the operator can find the edges of the previous area when he has to move into the next.

7 Refilling Mistblower

Emptying drums with a semi-rotary pump, is more convenient and quicker than using a tap. A tripod stand as shown in Diagram 26 is very useful when mistblowing. The machine can be started whilst it is standing on the platform.

8 Planning the Operation

Let it be assumed that a chemical cleaning operation is to take place amongst a crop of Norway spruce at 5 ft x 5 ft (1·5 m x 1·5 m) spacing, the average height of which is 5 ft (1·5 m). The weed species is a mixture of ash, hazel, willow and birch coppice, with an average height of 6 ft (1·8 m). Prior to spraying, racks have been cut 25 ft (7·6 m) apart, between two rows of Norway spruce and, as a result, ground conditions are such as to permit unimpeded walking. Calibration runs with water have determined that the rate of spraying per hectare is 180 litres (16 gallons per acre). Because the walking conditions are so good, it has been decided to use a nozzle that gives a fairly high output, in this example 72 litres (6·4 gallons) per hour. Further information given by these calibration runs is that a mistblower with a 2¼ gallon (10 litre) capacity and with this output will allow six lineal chains (120 m) to be sprayed before the tank empties. There is a ride at one side of the spraying area and 45 gallon (205 litre) drums can be dropped off where needed within the spraying area, these being transported by means of drum carriers (see Diagram 27) attached to a tractor three-point linkage. The other method by which the diluent can be conveyed into the area is the semi-rotary pump system (see Chapter 18, paras 5 and 6, pages 64–66.)

9 Using 45-gallon (205 litre) Drums

Diagram 13 shows the layout of the job. A boundary marked with twine has been laid out at right angles to the racks and parallel with the ride. On a line halfway between these two boundaries, i.e. three chains (60 m) from each, the 45-gallon (205 litre) drums have been laid 60 yd (55 m) apart at points A and B. The operator fills the mistblower at A, walks across to the first rack and commences spraying the swath to his left (1), upon reaching the ride, he turns, again spraying the swath to his left (2) until he is level with the 45-gallon (205 litre) drum. He then walks across to it, fills up, returns to the first rack and commences the area along the line of drums, spraying the swath to his left (3) until he reaches the line of twine. He turns again and sprays the swath to his left (4), until he comes level with the line of drums. After refilling he walks to the rack adjacent to the first and continues spraying, as described above, returning to Drum A each time he refills. However, when he has completed spraying the adjacent areas to rack Z, he will be 30 yds (say 30 m) from Drum A, so that instead of returning to this drum he walks across and starts to refill from Drum B, spraying in the same manner as described above.

10 Using a Bulk Supply Positioned on the Ride

Diagram 14 shows the layout of the job. The spraying is carried out in exactly the same way as decribed in para 9. The cross rack walking is no more than 30 yd (say 30 m) so that when the operator has worked this distance from the pump he must either withdraw it from the area and take it up the rack six chains (120 m) away from the first position A or else he must take it at right angles across to the second position at B. On flat ground, it is possible to pump through 500 ft (150 m) of hose and not lose much pressure, so that the pump can be carried across to several alternative positions without moving the trailer/tank.

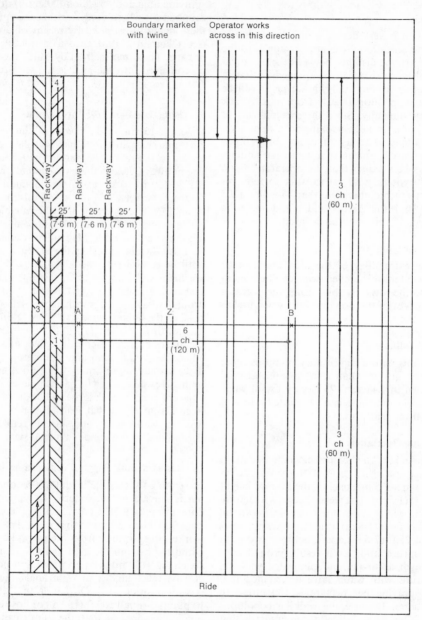

Diagram 13. Knapsack mistblowing—layout when using 45 gal (205 litre) drums

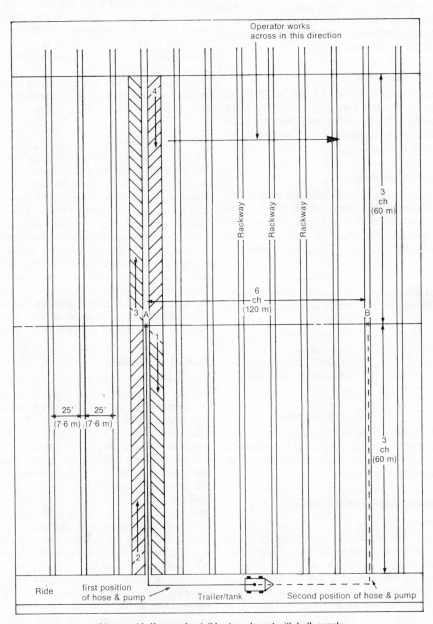

Operator works
across in this direction

Rackway

Rackway

Rackway

3
ch
(60 m)

6
ch
(120 m)

3 A

B

1

25'   25'
(7·6 m) (7·6 m)

3
ch
(60 m)

2

Ride   first position
of hose & pump   Trailer/tank   Second position of hose & pump

Diagram 14. Knapsack mistblowing—layout with bulk supply
positioned on ride

Chapter 12

GRANULAR HERBICIDE APPLICATORS

1 Introductory

A fair amount of success has been achieved in a wide range of grasses and herbaceous broadleaved weeds with the granular herbicide, chlorthiamid, marketed in Great Britain as Shellstar "Prefix".

2 Herbicide Specification

The specification for the use of Prefix is 55 lbs of granules to the treated acre (62 kg per hectare). Since one ounce (28 g) therefore treats between 5 and 6 square yards (4·2–5·0 sq m), a very precise distribution must be obtained.

3 Methods of Application

Two ways of applying chlorthiamid are used by the Forestry Commission, both mechanical. One machine is a motorised knapsack granule applicator (see Plate 46) and the other a tractor mounted granule applicator (plate 47). These are available as follows:

Supplier	Description
Horstine Farmery Ltd North Newbald York YO4 3SP	Horstine Farmery knap-sack granule applicator *Price* £85 ex-works.
	Description Model TMA 1 tractor mounted granule applicator *Price* £165 ex-works.

In mid-1972, the Stihl SG 17 knapsack mistblower was being tested for the application of chlorthiamid granules, a job it can do with a conversion kit available (see Chapter 11, para 1).

4 The Knapsack Applicator (Plate 46)

The Machine

The applicator works on the same principle as a mist-blower. A small 35 cc two-stroke engine drives a flexible fan which delivers a jet of air along a flexible tube and out through a fish-tail nozzle. The granules of the herbicide are contained in a hopper mounted above the engine and are let through a short plastic tube into the stream of air. This plastic tube is in two parts, and is separated by the metering mechanism and the on/off slide. The former consists of a disc stamped with varying sized holes, the pre-selection of which allows varying rates of flow of the granules. The flow of the granules is stopped and started by the on/off slide which is operated by means of a Bowden cable and a lever mounted on a short spur arm placed near to the operator's left hand. Engine revolutions are controlled by a throttle lever also mounted on the spur arm.

In mid-1972, the manufacturers were testing a prototype device which will convert the machine for the application of liquid herbicides.

Operation of Machine

The hopper is filled by removing the lid and pouring the granules from the sealed drum or bag. It is not necessary to filter the granules but it is advisable to stand up-wind when filling, since the dust, though not toxic, is unpleasant to smell. The lid is closed tightly and the bag or drum resealed since the granules quickly absorb atmospheric moisture. The engine is easily started with the recoil starter and the throttle opened as far as possible with the choke only being used when starting from cold. The carburettor slide is restricted from opening to its maximum by a small collar on the throttle cable so as to restrict the engine revolutions to about 4500 per minute to obtain a constant air speed.

Method of Working

The operator lifts the machine on to his back and adjusts the straps to his comfort. Because the machine weighs up to 45 lbs (20·4 kg) fully loaded, it is necessary to have a support of some kind (see Chapter 18, para 5) to take the weight while the machine is being filled. The operator walks to the left of the trees holding the nozzle directly above the trees at about 30″ (75 cm) from ground level, the granules being blown through the nozzle to cover a strip of 3 ft (0·90 m) wide. Any marked variation in nozzle height will give variation in width of application with consequent variation in application rates per hectare. Normally the machine is calibrated to allow the operator to walk at 2 mph (60 yards in 60 seconds – 3·2 km/h or 55 m in 60 seconds) and any gross variation from this speed will also affect the application rates. As the operator moves along the row the granules are spread in an even band over the trees. The plantation can be treated by the band method or the spot method. In the former, the granule flow lever is turned on at the beginning of the row and turned off at the end of the row. With spot treatment, an interrupted band is weeded with each strip being in the region of 3 ft (0·9 m) long (width of strip is about the same at 3 ft (0·9 m)) with the tree situated in the middle of the treated square. The operator must therefore turn the flow of granules on and off as he approaches and leaves the tree. This method is more difficult to learn than the band method because of a slight time lag between operating the slide and obtaining a response in the flow of granules: the degree of concentration needed to locate the tree and still retain a constant walking speed is higher but because less herbicide is used, it is the cheaper technique.

Calibration of Machine

To meet the exacting specification in para 2, the knapsack applicator requires careful adjustment. It is required to deliver an exact amount of granules to match the operator's walking speed and the width of the band. Any variation in walking speed or nozzle height will alter the application rate. Each machine needs to be calibrated at the beginning of the season because no two machines will be the same. Precise instructions are included in the operator's handbook, but to summarise, the flow of granules (timed over 5 minutes, the granules being collected in a drum and weighed) must match the desired application rate of 55 lbs per acre (62 kg per hectare) at the prescribed walking speed of 2 mph (3·2 km per hour). Thus the area treated in one hour will be a strip 2 miles long (3520 yards) by 1 yard wide and the correct flow rate can be calculated as follows:

$$\frac{3520 \text{ sq yds}}{4840 \text{ sq yds}} \times 55 \text{ lbs per acre} = 40 \text{ lbs per hour or 3 lbs } 5 \text{ oz in 5 minutes}$$

A disc setting is chosen which, according to a chart provided by the manufacturers, will give an output close to this amount. The output can be checked as in the previous paragraph. Further checks should be made during the season to confirm the original setting. Several dry runs should be made to allow the operator to become accustomed to walking at 2 mph (3·2 km/h). If the operator finds 2 mph too slow or the band width needs to be 4 ft (1·2 m) wide, the machine can easily be adjusted by the choice of another disc setting to compensate for the changes in specifications.

Alternative Techniques

The main choices are band treatment and spot treatment. However, satisfactory distribution depends on constant walking speed and, on very hilly ground, this is impossible to maintain in one or both directions. Here, an alternative technique is to approach the tree, stop, turn on the flow of granules and at the same time swing the nozzle through an arc which will spread the granules over the trees for the desired length of treatment. This method is of course imprecise, and it is difficult to check the application rate until it is too late. However, this technique has been used very successfully on a steep slope where it was impossible to maintain an even pace up hill.

5 The Tractor Mounted Applicator

The tractor mounted applicator (Plate 47) consists of a motorised fan mounted on a frame behind the tractor, blowing air through two flexible tubes fitted with fan-shaped nozzles. These nozzles are adjustable so that one or two rows of trees can be treated, each nozzle giving a 30″ (76 cm) spread. The flow of granules from the hopper to each flexible pipe is regulated to the speed of the tractor by means of a spiked land wheel. This applicator can be powered by a small agricultural tractor such as the Massey Ferguson MF 135 but can of course only be used where access by tractor is possible (see Chapter 7, para 2). It also requires substantial areas in which to work and which have been carefully prepared and planted.

Methods of Working

Two methods are practicable. In method one the tractor is driven over a row of trees and the nozzles so spaced to control a band of vegetation on either side. In this method, the risk to the trees is reduced while the width of controlled vegetation is increased. In method two, the tractor is driven between two rows and one row on either side is treated with each nozzle to give a 30″ (76 cm) controlled band along each row. Distribution achieved with method one is nearly as effective as with the knapsack machine. Some bucking of the tractor occurs when the wheels go over stumps but variation in width of treatment is not too critical when there are two bands 30″ (76 cm) wide along each side of the row. The untreated strip in the middle is likely to miss the trees from time to time.

When two rows are being treated at the same time (method two) and each row has only a 30″ (76 cm) swath of control, the combined effects of bucking and the varying distance between rows gives a considerably less efficient distribution of the granules in the rows.

Distribution of the chemical by the tractor mounted machine is cheaper than by knapsack.

6 New Developments

In late 1972, a gravity feed (non-powered) granular applicator was introduced in connection with Casoron G, a dichlobenil herbicide. It has been tested by the Forestry Commission. Enquiries can be addressed to Duphar-Midox Ltd, Smarden, Kent.

Chapter 13

LIVE REEL SPRAYERS

1 The Portable Sprayer

The increased use of knapsack sprayers has high-lighted the disadvantages of this type of equipment when used to apply large volumes of herbicide. They are heavy, must be refilled frequently, and the operator must wear a fair amount of protective clothing. It was clear that there was little to be gained by further development of this type of equipment, and, in 1967 the Forestry Commission's Research and Development Engineer developed a sledge mounted live reel sprayer which has been christened PHAROS (*Pump, Hose And Reel On Sledge*). It is designed with cut stump and basal bark treatment in mind, particularly for those areas where standing poles or rough or steep ground conditions restrict tractor access and make work with knapsack sprayers more laborious. Subsequently its potential for applying other herbicide treatments has become evident.

Pharos consists of a 110 cc Briggs and Stratton four-stroke engine, a pump, and a live reel with 500 ft (150 m) of ⅜th inch (9·5 mm) PVC (Poly Vinyl Chloride) hose, all mounted on a portable steel frame. The pump is plasticised and stainless steel couplings have been used which are resistant to corrosion from paraquat. The pump should be flushed with water and drained if out of use for some time. A self-sealing coupling is fitted to the end of the hose, to which is attached a 'Y' piece and two 120 ft x ¼" (37 m x 6 mm) EVA (Ethylene vinyl acetate) side hoses with standard hand lances. Small pressure control regulators attached to the lance handles enable pressures to be set correctly at the delivery end of the side lines. Separate 10 ft (3 m) suction and return pipes are fitted which are detachable from the pump. A second outlet is provided so that a second live reel can be used in a parallel or opposite direction. See Plates 48 and 49.

2 Sprayer Capabilities

The capabilities of the Pharos sprayer are as follows:

(a) Direct spraying can be carried out on slopes up to a height of 200′ (61 m) or more above Pharos. There is a reduction in pressure of approximately one pound per square inch for every 2 ft rise in height (about 0·12 kg/cm² for every metre) plus a friction loss of approximately 30 pounds per sq inch in 500 ft (2·1 kg/cm² in 152 m) of hose.

(b) Two or four operators are able to spray with Pharos, the extra equipment necessary for four-

man working, i.e. 20′ (6 m) and 80′ (24 m) extension hoses, crosspiece, two 120 ft (36 m) sidelines and lances, being available from the Dorman Sprayer Company Ltd. (See para 3 (a) below.)

(c) 2½–3 acres (1 hectare) can be sprayed at one set up thus keeping to a minimum the number of occasions when the main line is reeled in and Pharos moved.

(d) With an additional live reel (cost approx. £55) areas can be sprayed if tractor access is difficult to a distance of 1000′ (300 m) from Pharos.

(e) Water can be pumped from a natural source, e.g. river, dam or pond, into a container from which Pharos can be used for direct spraying. This may be of particular value in hilly districts.

3 Supplier

Pharos is available from:

Supplier	*Description*
The Dorman Sprayer Co Ltd.	Pharos sprayer complete
	Price
Brays Lane	2-man machine £396.00
Ely	4-man machine £444.50
Cambridgeshire.	

The following additional equipment is available:

(a) The extra equipment for four-man working (see paragraph 2) costing approximately £48.50.

(b) A portable 20-gallon (91 litres) reservoir fitted with adjustable legs and ball valve and a tap. This is mentioned in paragraph 2(e) above and is ideal for use with knapsack sprayers, where access for Pharos is difficult, or where a compartment is beyond the reach of the Pharos main line (500 feet – 150 m). The cost is approximately £15. This reservoir is shown in Plate 50.

(c) A drum coupling device is available for linking two 45-gallon (205 litre) drums.

4 Operating the Machine

A. Setting up Pharos

(1) Check all equipment, fuel, tools and spares available.

(2) Set out painted marking sticks in line in the direction in which the main hose is to be taken.

(3) Align the machine in the direction of spraying, and with the chemical supply.

(4) Check oil levels in engine and pump.

(5) Check petrol in fuel tank.

(6) Check that the amount of herbicide mixture is sufficient for the work period or spraying stint.

(7) Check and set pressure in air chamber.

(8) Connect suction and return pipes and place in herbicide supply.

(9) Check that pressure lever on pump is *off* and that tap on pump outlet is *on*.

(10) Start engine. Check that pump is primed by noting return of diluent to container.

(11) Set pressure on pump. Check gauge.

(12) Free live reel and pull out hose on to spray area.

(13) Check pressure at end of main hose (keep below 100 lbs per sq inch (7 kg/cm²) by adjusting pressure on pump).

(14) Insert Y-piece and sidelines.

(15) Check and set pressures at lances.

B. Pump pressures required for varied conditions

Notes

(a) An input of about 20 lbs per square inch (1·4kg per sq cm) is required on each sideline in order to maintain pressure at the lance.

(b) A loss of approximately 1 lb per square inch occurs for every 2′ rise (0·12 kg/cm² for every m rise) of the main hose above Pharos.

Table 8 shows pressures required to pump herbicide to two-man and four-man teams when they are working on a level with the machine and higher or lower than the machine.

TABLE 8

PUMPING PRESSURES: PHAROS

Pressure required to pump to men who are working	2 man team		4 man team	
	lbs/in²	kg/cm²	lbs/in²	kg/cm²
on a level with Pharos	70	4·9	110	7·7
50′ (15 m) above ,,	100	7·0	140	9·8
100′ (30 m) ,, ,,	120	8·4	160	11·2
200′ (61 m) ,, ,,	170	12·0	210	14·8
50′ (15 m) below ,,	50	3·5	90	6·3
100′ (30 m) ,, ,,	25	1·8	60	4·2
200′ (61 m) ,, ,,	10	0·7	20	1·4

C. Taking down Pharos to move

(1) Loop in sidelines and disconnect Y-piece from main hose.

(2) 1st operator walks back to Pharos with sidelines and Y-piece.

(3) 2nd operator takes each marking stick, measures across to the next line of advance of the main hose and sets them up.

(4) 2nd operator hauls in the main hose to each marking stick before moving the stick across to the next spraying block.

(5) 1st operator lifts suction pipe clear of diluent and allows residue to be pumped back.

(6) 1st operator stops engine and turns off tap on pump outlet to live reel.

(7) 1st operator disconnects suction and return hoses from pump and allows any diluent remaining to run back into container.

(8) 1st operator carries suction and return hoses and sidelines to next Pharos position.

(9) 1st operator winds in and places hose carefully on live reel assisted by 2nd operator who hauls in the main hose from the most suitable position.

(10) 1st and 2nd operators move Pharos to next spraying position.

Note: Replace bungs into drums.

5 Working Methods

A. Spraying of 100 per cent 2,4,5-T in paraffin as a Pre-Planting Treatment on Cut Stumps or as a Basal Bark Treatment.

Planning is essential in order to use Pharos to its best advantage, i.e. when the *full* length of the hose is utilized, and coupled with the supply of the required amount of diluent to *each* pumping point.

(a) Two-man working (See diagram 15)

The Y-piece attached to the main hose is carried out in a straight line at one chain (20 m) intervals in the direction of spraying, commencing at half a chain (10 m) inside the spraying area. The line of advance should be marked out previously with three or more painted marking sticks. At each stop, the two operators proceed in opposite directions at right angles to the main line for a distance of 1½ chains (30 m) spraying the half chain (10 m) back to their outward travel and the half chain (10 m) forward on their return gathering up the sideline as they do so. The two operators then pick up the Y-piece and walk on a chain (20 m) to the next step and repeat the spraying procedure until the full length of 500 feet (150 m) of the main line hose is unreeled. Over two acres (nearly 1 hectare) can be sprayed at one set up.

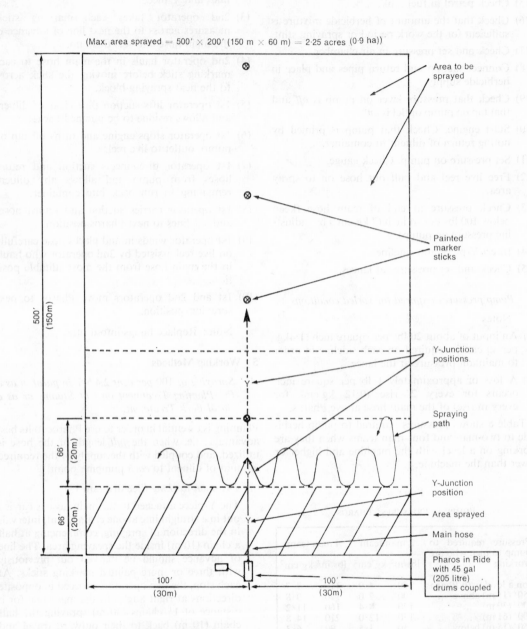

(Max. area sprayed = 500′ × 200′ (150 m × 60 m) = 2·25 acres (0·9 ha))

Area to be sprayed

Painted marker sticks

Y-Junction positions.

Spraying path

Y-Junction position

Area sprayed

Main hose

Pharos in Ride with 45 gal (205 litre) drums coupled

500′ (150m)

66′ (20m)

66′ (20m)

100′ (30m)

100′ (30m)

Diagram 15. Pharos sprayer and two men: cut stump and basal bark treatment: 100% 2,4,5-T in oil

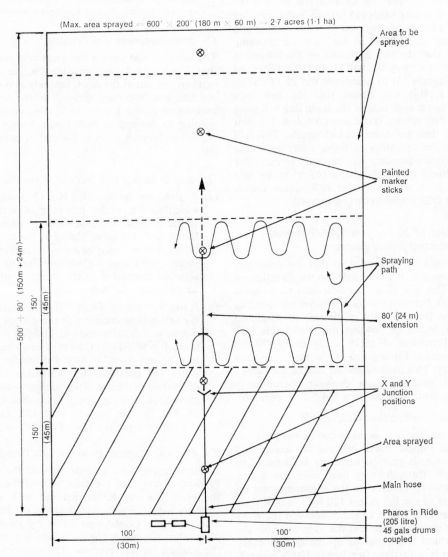

(Max. area sprayed = 600′ × 200′ (180 m × 60 m) = 2·7 acres (1·1 ha)

Area to be sprayed

Painted marker sticks

Spraying path

80′ (24 m) extension

X and Y Junction positions

Area sprayed

Main hose

Pharos in Ride (205 litre) 45 gals drums coupled

500′ + 80′ (150m + 24m)

150′ (45m)

150′ (45m)

100′ (30m)

100′ (30m)

Diagram 16. Pharos sprayer and four men: cut stump and basal bark treatment: 100% 2,4,5-T in oil (*b*) *Four-man working* (See diagram 16)

The 80 ft (24 m) extension hose is attached to the 3-way X-junction piece supplied, which is first inserted at the end of the main hose, the normal Y-piece being fitted to the end of the extension. The four operators haul out the main line in the direction of spraying so that the leading Y-junction is fifty yards (46 m) inside the spraying area. Sidelines are coupled to the main line and spraying carried out as for two-man working except that the two operators on the extension should first spray the half chain (10 m) forward (see diagram 16) to a distance out of 1½ chains (30 m); this will ensure that the two men spraying on each side of the main line will meet up as they return, and if one completes his stint he can then assist the man alongside. This will enable the operators to finish spraying at the same time when they will be ready to carry the main line a further 2¼ chains (45 m) to the next 'stop' from where another 6–7 square chains (about 0·25 hectares) can be sprayed.

B. *Spraying of* 50 *per cent* 2,4,5-T *in water as a post planting foliage treatment*

Pharos should be positioned so that the main line can be taken out at right angles to the direction of planting. This will allow the operators to progress up and back between the rows without the sidelines fouling the trees. Supply of diluent in 45-gallon (205 litre) drums or bowsers must take this into account. Provision of racks at 3½ chain (70 m) intervals to ease hauling out of the main line may be necessary. This method should also be used when basal bark spraying as a cleaning operation in plantations (with 100 per cent 2,4,5-T in paraffin).

(*a*) *Two-man working* (See diagram 17)

The main line hose is taken out across the rows and the Y-piece placed between the second and third rows. It may be necessary beforehand to cut racks through every third inter row space. Operators spray between the adjoining rows on one side to the full extent 120 ft (37 m) of their sidelines and return to spray between the rows on the opposite side and the vegetation in the row behind them, picking up the sideline every few yards with their free hand. The Y-piece is then taken on to the centre one of the next three inter row spaces and spraying continued as before and so on to the full extent of the main line, a total of 2½ acres (about 1 hectare).

(*b*) *Four-man working* (diagram 18)

With the 20 ft (6 m) extension and Y-piece the leading pair of operators work between the rows

of trees three spaces ahead of the second pair. When the four operators have sprayed back to the main line they move on with the main hose to spray the next six rows. If the 80 ft (24 m) extension is first attached to the main line an area of approximately three acres – 8¾ x 3½ chains (1·25 hectares – 175 m x 70 m) can be sprayed before Pharos has to be moved.

C. *Spot Treatment with Paraquat*

The working method for this treatment is similar to that detailed for foliage spraying, i.e. the main hose is taken out across the rows, but only two rows (one out and one back) are sprayed by the operator at each move of the Y-piece. A Politec or wash bowl is fitted to the end of each lance. Pharos must be flushed with clean water at the end of each working day.

D. *Use of Pharos with Natural Water Supply*

(*a*) Pharos is equipped with a 10 ft (3 m) suction pipe which facilitates the pumping of water direct from a natural source such as river, dam or pond; the return pipe being placed in the container to be filled. *Care must be taken* to ensure that the suction filter cage is clean and that no chemical solution remaining in the pump is allowed to contaminate the water supply.

(*b*) A free flow nozzle if supplied can be inserted into the self-sealing coupling at the end of the main line to enable containers to be filled at any distance (up to 500 ft) (150 m) from Pharos. This may be very useful in hilly districts for pumping water (or paraffin from 45-gallon (205 litre) drums) on to the site to where Pharos can now be moved for direct spraying. A maximum pressure of 300 lbs per square inch (21 kg/cm²) is available for rapid filling of containers.

E. *Use with Portable Reservoir* (see Para 3 (b))

If the spraying area extends beyond the range of Pharos, coverage of the area beyond the reach of the main line can be carried out with knapsack sprayers with the aid of a 20-gallon (91 litre) portable reservoir. Continuous filling by Pharos takes place when the end of the main hose is connected to the adaptor on the reservoir. The reservoir is fitted with adjustable legs and has a ball valve which cuts off the supply when it is full. Knapsack sprayers can then be filled by means of a wide bore tap which gives a delivery of 3 gallons (13·5 litres) per minute with full reservoir.

F. *Use with Two Live Reels*

If a second live reel is available, it can be connected

Plate 17. The Wolseley 30″ (76 cm) Clearway rotating blade brushcutter. WS 2/36/20

Plate 17A. The Wolseley "Clearway HS" with hydrostatic drive. WS 3/19/16A

D*

Plate 18. The Turner 30″ flail mower. WS 2/41/2

Plate 19. The underside of the 30″ (76 cm) Turner flail mower showing some of the 48 double
L-shaped flails suitable for grass and light herbaceous weeds. WS 4/80

Plate 20. The Wolseley Swipe Jungle Buster cutting a grass ride. It cuts by means of rotating chains.

D 6007

Plate 21. The Bush Hog rotating blade brushcutter. (In this photograph, the power take-off shaft is not correctly guarded.) WS 1/18/18

Plate 22. A Bush Hog fitted with torque limiting clutch and power take-off shaft guard.   WS 4/81/1

Plate 23. The F E S Standard rotary brushcutter.
WS 2/33/2

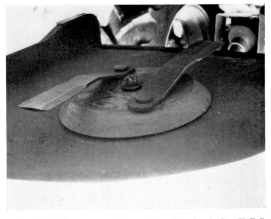

Plate 24. The saucer-like cutting head of the F E S brushcutter. That of the Bush Hog is similar. WS 2/33/4

Plate 25. A narrow gauge 4′ (1·2 m) wide rotating blade weeding machine working behind a Massey Ferguson MF 135 Vineyard tractor. WS 4/82

Plate 26. The same machine working with a Holder A20 frame steered tractor. WS 2/36/23

Plate 27. The Wilder Rainthorpe Scrub-Masta '40' flail-type weeding machine.

Plate 27A. The Wilder Rainthorpe Scrub-Masta '40' showing the flails. WS 3/13/17

Plate 28. An experimental front mounted brushcutter based on a McCormick International 523 tractor. The cutter is powered hydraulically. WS 2/86/20

Plate 29. The hinged guard to the cutter blades which lifts to apply tension to coppice during cutting. WS 2/87/8

Plate 30. The Mk I grass roller. WS 2/36/21

Plate 31. The Mk II hydraulically operated double grass roller. WS 2/78/15

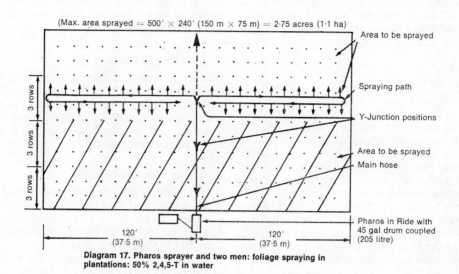

(Max. area sprayed = 500′ × 240′ (150 m × 75 m) = 2·75 acres (1·1 ha))

- Area to be sprayed
- Spraying path
- Y-Junction positions
- Area to be sprayed
- Main hose
- Pharos in Ride with 45 gal drum coupled (205 litre)

3 rows | 3 rows | 3 rows

120′ (37·5 m)   120′ (37·5 m)

Diagram 17. Pharos sprayer and two men: foliage spraying in plantations: 50% 2,4,5-T in water

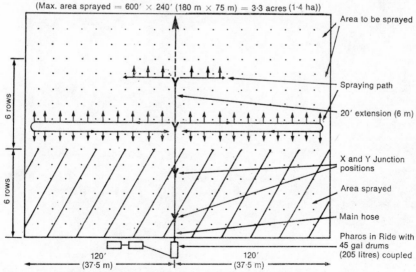

(Max. area sprayed = 600′ × 240′ (180 m × 75 m) = 3·3 acres (1·4 ha))

- Area to be sprayed
- Spraying path
- 20′ extension (6 m)
- X and Y Junction positions
- Area sprayed
- Main hose
- Pharos in Ride with 45 gal drums (205 litres) coupled

6 rows | 6 rows

120′ (37·5 m)   120′ (37·5 m)

Diagram 18. Pharos sprayer and four men: foliage spraying in plantations: 50% 2,4,5-T in water

to the second outlet on the pump and used either in parallel or in a different direction to the first. Where tractor access is difficult it may be useful to carry out the second live reel into the wood and connect it to the end of the main line hose. Direct spraying is then possible to a distance of 1,000 ft (300 m) with two or four men, increasing the pump pressure as necessary.

G. Supply of Diluent

When using two live reels or with four men working on the one main line, well over 200 gallons (900 litres) of diluent can be sprayed during a working day. As a 45-gallon (205 litre) drum can be emptied within the hour, it will require a walk back to Pharos by one of the operators in order to change over the suction and return pipes to a full drum. This problem can be overcome by supplying the diluent in a bowser or a 200 or more gallon (900 or more litres) tank on a trailer, but will require a tractor when the diluent has to be moved, with Pharos, to the next block to be sprayed. Alternatively two drums can be linked by means of a short length of hose fitted with two adaptors which plug into the 1 inch bung holes at the end of the drums. Ninety gallons (410 litres) are now available for spraying. If a small quantity of liquid remains in a drum, it can readily be emptied during a break period by taking out the return hose and inserting it into another container.

H. Use in cold weather

If water is used as a diluent during cold weather, ensure that the pump, suction and return hoses are well drained after use and, if possible, place Pharos overnight in a well sheltered store. If the main line is frozen, pull out the hose from the live reel in hanks and allow it to thaw.

6 Trailer Mounted Live Reel Sprayer

An experimental version of 'Pharos' named 'Pharot' – *Pump Hose And Reel On Trailer* – was built. The machine was bolted on to a 200-gallon (900 litre) Land Rover trailer. See Plate 52. A suitable trailer is described in Chapter 18, para 2.

A live reel sprayer mounted on a tractor is described in Chapter 15, para 3, page 54.

Chapter 14

TRACTOR MOUNTED MISTBLOWERS

1 Introductory

Where access for a tractor is possible, there are considerable advantages in using a tractor mounted mistblower in circumstances where a knapsack mist-blower would otherwise have been used. Tractor mounted mistblowers have been used for some years by fruit growers and market gardeners for spraying pesticides but their use in forestry is comparatively new. The Forestry Commission has tested three types of mistblower, and all have required consider-able modification to suit them to the task in hand. The most suitable machine is the Drake and Fletcher Victair. (See Plate 51).

Supplier	Description
Drake & Fletcher Ltd Maidstone, Kent	Victair Standard modified as below
	Price £481.75 including modifica-tions. (a)–(d) below.

The machine was modified prior to delivery by the manufacturers as follows:

(a) An outlet designed for spraying coffee plan-tations was modified for forest use by reducing the deflection angle to 20 degrees.

(b) No galvanised parts were used.

(c) All washers and fittings were oil resistant.

(d) The standard pump was replaced by a small gear pump with a maximum output of 590 litres per hour at 690 kN/m² (130 gallons per hour at 100 lbs per square inch).
Further modifications made by the Forestry Commission were as follows:—

(e) A Massey Ferguson drawbar was permanently attached.

(f) A self-refill hose and strainer were fitted.

(g) The pump was guarded.

2 Description

The Victair has a 100-gallon (455 litre) capacity tank which is mounted tucked well into the back of the tractor giving good tractor stability. A single fan feeds two outlets which can point horizontally for foliar spraying or vertically for spraying of cut stumps before planting. The spray liquid is injected into the airstream by five nozzles on each outlet. Output control is achieved either by altering the screw-down pressure control valve or by changing the nozzle discs to different apertures. Agitation of the herbicide in the tank is provided from the pressure relief valve overflow.

The tractor used should be a Massey Ferguson MF 165 or equivalent. If a Massey Ferguson MF 135 or equivalent is used, it should be weighted at the front end. The linch pins should be replaced by self-locking nuts and bolts to prevent the machine becoming uncoupled. A tractor speed of 3·2 km/h (2 mph) will give 2,000 engine revs. per minute which is the correct power take off speed for the Victair. Powered refill time is 20 minutes during which time the driver is either resting or engaged on ancillary work.

3 Spraying Cut Stumps before Planting using 2,4,5-T in Paraffin

(a) The mistblower should be carried as high as possible on the hydraulic lift to obtain the required width of treatment, i.e. 10 ft (3 m).

(b) With the air outlets used vertically, there is no need to block off the top one. Herbicide is fed to the nozzles in the lower outlet only by setting the feed tap accordingly.

(c) The lowest pressure reading should be selected to give the required output. Drift can be con-siderably reduced by blocking off half of the air intake by means of for example a piece of hard-board. This will increase the droplet size.

(d) *The mistblower must never be lowered to the ground with the outlets vertical.* If it is the outlets and nozzles will be damaged.

(e) Any large stumps, not directly sprayed due to the tractor going round them, will not be killed and should be treated separately.

Pre-planting spraying can be carried out using 17 litres of 2,4,5-T in 340 litres of paraffin per hectare. (1·5 gals in 30 gals per acre). Where the woody vegetation is moderately resistant or resistant, the amount of herbicide should be increased to 22 litres per hectare. (2 gals per acre).

4 Foliar Spraying using 2,4,5-T in Water

(a) The outlets should be set horizontally and both sets of nozzles brought into use.

(b) The mistblower should be carried level on the tractor hydraulics.

Assuming vegetation cover to be fairly even, an

application rate of diluted herbicide of 100 litres per hectare (9 gals per acre) can be used and a swath width of 15 m (16 yds) providing the weed growth is not more than 2 m (say 6 ft) high. Where the weed growth is more than 2 m (say 6 ft) high the swath width should be 10 m (3½ yds). 4·5–7·0 litres of 2,4,5-T emulsifiable ester per hectare (3–5 pints per acre) should be used. Where access racks are necessary they can be cut with a tractor powered brushcutter (see Chapter 7). Wind can have a considerable effect on coverage; when the tractor is moving at right angles to the wind, the spray pattern from the windward side is reduced whilst that on the leeward side is extended. It is better not to spray in a wind in excess of 5 mph (8 km/h).

5 Foliar Spraying of Bramble in Mature Conifer Plantations

Tractor mistblowing of bramble to give access is highly effective. A complete breakdown of the dead material should take place within 18 months of spraying. Up to 3 sprayings can be carried out and still show a cost saving over other treatments such as hand or machine cutting, or additional payments (such as "bramble money") to chainsaw operators for the inconvenience during thinning.

6 Logistics

It is recommended that the bulk supply of herbicide should be pre-mixed at the forest depot and transported to the site by a 250-gallon (1136 litre) bowser which can be towed by the mistblower tractor. The bowser should be sited as close to the spraying site as possible to reduce ineffective travelling time to a minimum.

7 Output

The effectiveness of a mistblower depends more on the volume of air moved than the initial speed. The size of the Victair outlet is more than seven times that of other machines tested and it is not cluttered by injectors, etc. Calibration tests of the actual output against the calculated setting proved the machine to be extremely accurate.

TABLE 9
VICTAIR MISTBLOWER – TOTAL NOZZLE OUTPUTS

| Pressure setting | Total output in litres per minute | | | | | |
| | 5 nozzles: 4 hole backplate | | | 10 nozzles: 4 hole backplate | | |
	No. 4 disc	No. 6 disc	No. 8 disc	No. 4 disc	No. 6 disc	No. 8 disc
10	5·18	9·13	20·13	10·35	18·25	40·25
9	4·83	8·53	18·70	9·65	17·05	37·40
8	4·48	7·73	17·20	8·95	15·45	34·40
7	4·13	7·33	15·70	8·26	14·65	31·40
6	3·86	6·70	13·85	7·71	13·40	27·70
5	3·45	6·05	12·38	6·90	12·10	24·75
4	3·00	5·46	11·08	6·00	10·91	22·15
3	2·73	4·83	9·48	5·45	9·65	18·95

Where Table 9 gives an alternative setting to obtain the same output, the setting with the lowest pressure should be selected to reduce drift.

8 Calculation of Nozzle Settings

(a) Distance travelled per hectare sprayed:

$$\frac{\text{Area in sq m}}{\text{Width of pass in m}}$$

(b) Distance travelled in one minute:

$$\frac{\text{Speed in km/h } \times 1{,}000}{60}$$

(c) Time to spray one hectare:

$$\frac{\text{Distance travelled to spray 1 hectare}}{\text{Distance travelled in 1 minute}}$$

(d) Output required per minute:

$$\frac{\text{Application rate (litres per hectare)}}{\text{Spraying time per hectare}}$$

(e) Mistblower setting:

Having calculated the output required, the appropriate pressure setting figure is selected from table 9. In this case, 10 nozzles with No 4 discs give a pressure setting of:

Example

$$\frac{10{,}000}{15} = 666 \cdot 7 \text{ metres}$$

$$\frac{3 \cdot 2 \times 1{,}000}{60} = 53 \cdot 3 \text{ metres}$$

$$\frac{666 \cdot 7}{53 \cdot 3} = 12 \cdot 5 \text{ minutes}$$

$$\frac{100}{12 \cdot 5} = 8 \cdot 0 \text{ litres per min.}$$

$6\frac{1}{2}$

Chapter 15

TRACTOR MOUNTED HIGH VOLUME SPRAYING APPARATUS

1 General

The Forestry Commission has experimented with tractor mounted high volume spraying equipment as an alternative to using knapsack sprayers. The essential feature is that tractor access must be possible. The main advantage of this type of equipment is for the application of 2,4,5-T diluted with paraffin to cut stumps because of the reduced time spent in refilling.

2 Equipment

Such equipment usually consists of a tank to carry the diluted herbicide and a pump operated by the tractor power take-off. In its simplest form, two hoses and lances with pressure reduction gear can be fitted. In this instance the crew consists of a tractor driver plus two men spraying. This equipment is shown in Plate 53.

3 Modifications

To improve these machines, the Forestry Commission developed one which can be used as a live reel sprayer, rather like a tractor-mounted Pharos. Two or four hand-held lances can be connected by means of instant sealing couplings fitted to a bar at the front of the tractor. This permits its use for applying 2,4,5-T in paraffin to cut stumps (see Plate 54) or, if the lances are fitted with suitable guards, for the application of paraquat (see Plate 55).

4 Enquiries

Anyone wishing to follow up the possible use of such equipment should in the first instance contact the manufacturers of the basic sprayer:
E. Allman & Co. Ltd.
Birdham Road,
Chichester, Sussex. PO20 7BT.

Chapter 16

AERIAL APPLICATION

1 General

The Forestry Commission's Work Study Branch has not so far studied aerial application of herbicides and at present the Forestry Commission does not use this technique. No handbook of this kind would however be complete without some mention of the subject and the Commission has experience from the past to call upon. Aerial application is not the cheap means it may seem (see costs in Chapter 21, para 18 (iv)). It does however have the advantages of being independent of terrain and, because of necessity, it is contracted work and only minimal demands are made on one's own staff. It is sometimes necessary to provide men to act as markers. Weather must be just right for aerial spraying and sometimes a number of abortive attempts are made before the right day comes. This waiting can be expensive in labour and supervision costs.

2 Points to be taken into Account when deciding to use Aerial Spraying

(a) Plan well ahead. As it is a foliage spraying technique, the last two weeks of August and September are the best times of application in planted areas, and from mid June to the end of July for preplanting spraying. You will need to contact the contractor giving him earliest and latest possible dates. Quite small areas say 200 acres (80 hectares) can be sprayed.

(b) Notify your neighbours what you are doing and when you intend to do it. Give them time to harvest their crops in fields adjoining your woodland. They may need to move stock out of the adjoining field temporarily. Most contractors will do a prior inspection (sometimes with the forester) and decide which neighbouring crops are susceptible and then *they* will contact the owners.

(c) Make sure that you have adequate insurance cover either built into the contract or separately. Unintentional damage to neighbours' or your own property can be expensive.

(d) You may wish to ask several firms to quote, in which case you will call for estimates and compare them before deciding which to accept.

(e) Most contractors will locate their own landing strip but your knowledge can help. The nearer the airstrip, the cheaper the price. Contractors will also supply herbicide but may call upon you to supply the diluent (water).

(f) Weather can play havoc with Contractor's arrangements and can make it necessary to work at weekends. This could give you problems with the men you intend to employ as markers. Simple clear instructions are given to the markers and they are supplied with Da-Glo painted cards which should be affixed to poles. It is useful to ascertain the width of the band to be sprayed with each pass of the aircraft (usually 18 ft (5·5 m)); poles can then be cut to this size so that not only can they carry the card but can also be used to measure the swaths. Wind speeds of up to 10 knots are usually acceptable when spraying. Spraying should be carried out in a wind of 10–15 knots only if it is blowing away from susceptible crops. Winds at ground level are usually least at dawn and dusk. Hence the first two or three hours after sunrise and the last hour or two before sunset are times most suitable for spraying and when risk of drift is minimal but there may be difficulty in obtaining men to act as markers at these times. It should be clearly laid down in the contract that the pilot of the aircraft has the last word when the decision whether to spray or not is taken.

(g) Full protective clothing for markers will be necessary – see Chapter 19.

3 Contractors

There is a national association to which aerial spraying contractors can belong but not all contractors are members. Anyone wishing to make contact with a firm can consult the yellow pages of the telephone directory or write to:

> The Secretary
> The National Association of Agricultural
>   Contractors
> 140 Bensham Lane
> Thornton Heath
> Surrey.

4 Effects and Results

The full effect of the spraying will not appear until the following mid-summer although it is possible to gain an idea of how much coverage has been achieved from the effects on the leaves. Sometimes the spraying swaths will overlap in which case crop trees could receive double dosage which can result in considerable browning of needles. Sometimes the opposite will happen and certain weed growth will receive no cover.

5 Helicopters or Fixed Wing Aircraft?

Generally fixed wing aircraft seem to be more effective because they give a greater measure of control over the rate of application than helicopters; they are also cheaper. The turbulence caused by helicopter rotors is inclined to blow spray all over the place and result in patchiness. There is also a danger of increased drift.

6 The Herbicide

Foliage spraying in crops has been carried out at 3–5 pints of 2,4,5-T emulsifiable ester in 5–10 gallons of water per acre (4–7 litres in 56–112 litres of water per hectare), and pre-planting applications at 5 pints of 2,4,5-T emulsifiable ester in 8 gallons of water and two gallons of oil per acre (7 litres in 90 litres of water and 22 litres of oil per hectare). The oil is added as a sticker and can be omitted. Aerial spraying is relatively inexpensive particularly in difficult cleaning situations but rarely gives as complete a kill as ground spraying. It is best therefore to think in terms of two or may be three sprayings with the minimum dose rate rather than one attempt at a complete kill. Plates 56 and 57 show aerial spraying of 2,4,5-T in water on woody weed growth at Wicken Wood, Hazelborough Forest (Northants).

Chapter 17

ULTRA LOW VOLUME SPRAYING TECHNIQUES

1 General

The newest of the spraying techniques and still largely experimental in forestry, ultra low volume spraying is well established in many fields, especially in tropical agriculture, for the spraying of fungicides and insecticides.

2 Droplets from Conventional Sprayers

Conventional application techniques such as knapsack sprayers and mistblowers create a wide range of droplet sizes as well as producing a rather large mean droplet size. The very small droplets produced by these sprayers, particularly mist-blowers, disappear as "drift" into the distance sometimes to the detriment of neighbouring crops, and the large drops fall to the ground either directly or by run off, thus wasting expensive chemical.

Water is used as a diluent and even droplets which are of a suitable size when they leave the mistblower are quickly subjected to evaporation especially on a hot summer day. The resultant fine droplets are thus composed mainly of the active agent which may eventually come to earth miles from the intended target. The droplets produced by conventional sprayers vary in size according to the size of the outlet, the pressure and the diluent. For example, a knapsack sprayer will produce droplets with a mean diameter of 460–760 μm, while the knapsack mistblower creates droplets with a mean diameter of 220–450 μm, depending on the nozzle used.

(Note: one micrometre (μm) = 1 micron (μ) =
$\dfrac{1}{1000}$ th of a millimetre.)

3 Droplets from Ultra Low Volume Sprayers

Ultra low volume applicators produce droplets in a narrower size range around a mean diameter of approximately 100 μm because they are formulated in a non-evaporating oil; to some extent the droplet size can be altered by the operator. With 100 μm droplets, about 50 are deposited on a square cm of leaf surface when spraying 1 litre per hectare. The space between the droplets is about 1 millimetre. This shows up well in Plate 58 which is reproduced at 1$\frac{1}{2}$ x magnification. Note also the evenness of the droplet size.

4 Advantages of ULV Droplets

Because volume varies according to the cube of the droplet diameter, even the mean droplets of conventional applicators are wasteful. The bigger droplets contain much more diluent than the more concentrated much smaller ULV droplet. For example, a 600 μm droplet from a knapsack sprayer contains only 2% of herbicide whereas the same volume delivered by a ULV applicator consists of 1000 separate droplets each of which contains 15 times the amount of herbicide as in the 600 μm droplet of the conventional applicator which will consist for the greater part of diluent which has been expensive to transport to the site and may serve little useful purpose.

5 Control over Drift

In the correct meteorological conditions the constant droplet size of the ULV sprayer gives greater control over drift. A droplet with a diameter of 100 μm has a steady fall rate of 250 mm per second. Hence a droplet released at 2 m (6$\frac{1}{2}$ feet) above ground level will take 8 seconds to reach the ground in still air conditions. If the wind speed is say 5 km/h (say 3 mph), theoretically the droplet would deposit (in the absence of intervening vegetation) at about 11·1 m (33 feet) from the sprayer.

6 Machine Principles

ULV machines are basically simple. The herbicide feeds under gravity on to a disc with a serrated edge which is rotated (electrically or mechanically) at a set speed, the speed of rotation determining the droplet size. The droplets so produced are dispersed either by the wind or by a fan set behind the rotating disc.

7 The Battery-powered Applicator

The simplest sprayer (Plate 59) consists of a 1·5 m (5 feet) long hollow plastic tube containing 8 x 1$\frac{1}{2}$ volt batteries, a small motor and a slightly conical serrated disc fixed to one end of the tube. The motor rotates the serrated disc at approximately 7000 rpm when a switch is operated. A one litre bottle of prepared herbicide is screwed behind the disc which, when inverted, feeds herbicide (by gravity) at rates varying between $\frac{1}{2}$–3 ml per second on to the rotating disc. The operator then walks up and down the plantation across the wind allowing the herbicide to drift on to the weeds. The bottle empties in between 5·6 and 34 minutes of spraying time. In that time it will have produced two thousand million 100 μm diameter droplets. Knapsack containers carrying a reserve supply of 5 or 10 litres (about 1 or 2 gals.) are being developed. See Plate 60.

E

8 Other Equipment

The equipment described in para 7 is the only type used at present by the Forestry Commission, but for completeness, information about other available apparatus is given.

To improve leaf cover at close range, to increase the height at which droplets are released, and to increase the range of the applicator, a fan-assisted machine has been developed which is powered by a small two-stroke petrol engine (Plate 61). A further development mounts this equipment on a small wheeled carriage so that it can be towed through the forest (Plate 62).

9 Tractor and Aircraft Mounting

Where conditions permit, tractor mounting increases the range and capacity of ULV equipment. One machine (Plate 63) fitted with two rear mounted fans which are angled so that a swath on either side of a rack can be sprayed (as with a tractor mounted mist-blower). A development of this machine fitted with a single rear mounted oscillating fan (which reduces machine costs) is shown in Plate 64. Equipment for fitting to aircraft is also available.

10 Producers of Equipment

The main producers in Great Britain of ULV equipment are:

(i) Micron Sprayers Ltd.
   Bromyard
   Herefordshire.
   The distributors in the United Kingdom for their equipment are:
   J. H. B. Implements Ltd.
   Ickburgh
   Thetford
   Norfolk
   1P26 5JG.
   They manufacture equipment as follows:

Name	Type	Cost
ULVA	–hand held, battery operated.	
Mini Micron	–hand held, 2-stroke engine powering a fan.	
Micronette Mk 5	–pedestrian controlled, one wheeled, 2-stroke engine powering a fan.	Apply to manufacturers
Mantis	– tractor powered, double fan.	
Oscillating Mantis	–tractor powered single oscillating fan.	

(ii) Turbair Ltd.
   Britannic House
   Waltham Cross, Herts.
   The distributors in the United Kingdom for their equipment are:
   Pan Britannica Industries Ltd.
   Britannic House
   Waltham Cross, Herts.
   Their range of machines includes the following:

Turbair "X"	– hand held, lightweight, 12 volt battery operated without fan (Power pack extra).	Apply to manufacturer
Turbair Tot 2S	– hand held, 2-stroke petrol engine driven. Fan assisted droplet dispersal.	£59.50
Turbair Scamp 240	– hand held, mains electric, 240 volt 300 watt (110 volt model available). Fan assisted dispersal	£26.50
Turbair Imp 12	– hand held, 12 volt, 10 amp battery operated. Fan assisted droplet dispersal.	£32.00
	Power pack	£12.00

11 Foliage Spraying of Woody Weeds in Conifer Crops

The herbicide used is 2,4,5-T formulated with a non-phytotoxic oil which evaporates only slowly, so that the droplet size remains constant after leaving the applicator and sticks to foliage thereby increasing rainfastness and spray retention. Ten litres of this formulation contains 3 kg of 2,4,5-T active ingredient and the recommendation when foliage spraying of hardwood weeds in conifer crops is 7 litres per treated hectare (5 pints per acre). It is available as follows:

Supplier	Description
B. P. Trading Ltd.	Silvapron 'T'
Agricultural Branch	Price
Britannic House	5 gal. drum, £4.75 per gal.
Moor Lane	45 gal. drum, £4.60 per gal.
London EC2Y 9BU	

12 Control of Heather in Conifer Crops

In this case the recommended herbicide is 40% 2,4-D ester formulated in non-phytotoxic oil at the rate of 10 litres per treated hectare (5 pints per acre). It is available as follows:

Supplier
B.P. Trading Ltd.
Agricultural Branch
Britannic House
Moor Lane
London EC2Y 9BU

Description
Silvapron 'D'
Price
5 gal. drum, £3 per gal.
45 gal. drum, £2.85 per gal.

Details of best time of application using ULV equipment in the control of heather are given in Chapter 11, para 2, page 38.

13 Method of Application

As stated in para 1, this technique is still experimental. Anyone who wishes to try it is therefore advised to contact the distributors of the equipment before doing so. Their names and addresses are given in para 10.

Meteorological conditions required for spraying are a wind speed at ground level of between 2 and 7 miles per hour (3–11 km/h) to ensure that the droplets disperse properly and impact onto the vegetation. Wind speed can be measured with a wind meter and wind direction with smoke pellets. A safety belt of 100 metres (say 100 yds) in the lee of the sprayed area is recommended. Most droplets deposit within 40 metres (40 yards) of the applicator and no effects have been found beyond 80 metres (80 yards) even in trials done in wind speeds well above those prescribed. Spraying can be done when the vegetation is wet or during light drizzle but it should not be attempted in calm conditions. In essence, the operator walks at 3 km/h (say 2 mph) roughly at right angles to the wind holding the applicator at the appropriate height dependent on crop, wind speed, etc. When treating foliage, he sprays a 5 m (16 feet) wide swath down-wind from himself, covering the area in a series of such bands, each of which is up-wind from its predecessor. As a man can treat one hectare ($2\frac{1}{2}$ acres) in an hour easily, an output of more than 5 hectares (12 acres) per day is achievable. When spraying heather, single lane application (i.e. between 2 rows or trees) is the recommended method for best results. An output of $2\frac{1}{2}$ hectares ($7\frac{1}{2}$ acres) per day is possible. At the time of writing, multiple row application was under trial.

Whatever the application, adequate operator training is essential.

14 Protection of the Operator

Protective clothing is desirable but a major advance in the acceptability to operators of chemical spraying is made possible by ULV application. Due to the small amounts applied and the method of application in which the spray is deliberately allowed to drift away from the operator, clothing which does not have to contend with gross spillage has been developed. Although the material stops liquid, it allows air to pass through and this makes it as comfortable to wear as a cotton garment. In addition, face shield, mask, gloves and oil proof boots are recommended. This clothing is on trial for a period of two years beginning in 1973. Details are as follows:

Suit
    Supplier
    Abridge Overalls, Ltd
    Burgess Hill
    Sussex

    Description
    Jalite ULV Suit
    Price
    £9 approximately

Face Shield (B.S. 2092:1967)
    Supplier
    Safety Products, Ltd
    Holmthorpe Avenue
    Redhill, Surrey

    Description
    Clearways face shield
    Type PE 14/84
    Price
    £1

Gloves
    Supplier
    James North & Sons, Ltd
    P.O. Box No. 3
    Hyde
    Cheshire SR14 1RL

    Description
    Type 485 Northgrip
    Gloves
    Price
    31p per pair.

Mask
    Supplier
    Herts Packaging Co, Ltd
    53 London Road
    St. Albans
    Herts.

    Description
    3M 8500 non-toxic
    particle mask.
    Price
    £3.88 per box of 50
    plus postage.

Oil Proof Boots
See Chapter 19, para 6.

The clothing listed in this paragraph is also available from J.H.B. Implements, Ltd., Ickburgh, Thetford, Norfolk, IP26 5JG.

Washing facilities are necessary—see Chapter 19, para 11, page 75.

15 Future of the Technique

It is too soon to say that here is a technique which can be used on a wide scale; suffice to say that there is a reasonable degree of hope for its future in forest applications. Extensive trials are being carried out in 1973 and 1974.

16 Further Reading

The following papers give more details:

"Some thoughts on the concept of ULD (Ultra Low Dosage) spraying", E. J. Bals, *FAO Conference of International Organisations, February* 1971. (The author has quoted from this paper liberally above and offers his acknowledgements, to Mr Bals.) "The Principles of and New Developments in Ultra Low Volume Spraying", E. J. Bals, *Proceedings of the 5th British Insecticide and Fungicide Conference* 1969.

Chapter 18

LOGISTICS: THE PROBLEM OF SUPPLY

1 Mixing of Herbicides with Diluents

The herbicide should be mixed in bulk rather than at each filling of the sprayer. The latter method is time-consuming and a greater degree of accuracy can be achieved with bulk mixing. The minimum quantity that should be mixed is 40 gallons (182 litres), but better still, if a 250-gallon (1136 litres) trailer/tank or bowser is being used, then this quantity should be mixed provided it can be used within a week. A further advantage of bulk mixing at a depot is that agitation takes place within the containers whilst they are being taken to the spraying site and this helps to obtain a thorough mix of chemical and diluent. The mixture should be stirred every day before use. Mixing should be carried out by a supervisor or a trained worker to reduce the risk of accidents. It is appreciated however that bulk mixing may not always be possible or practical. Pre-mixing is not at present recommended for atrazine (see Chapter 9, para 8). When mixing concentrated herbicides with diluent, the concentrate should never be put into the mixing container first. This is because, when the first few drops of diluent contact the concentrate, crystals can sometimes be formed which are difficult to break down and which may clog the spraying equipment. Probably the best way to deal with mixing is to half fill the transporting container with diluent at the depot, add the concentrate, and complete the filling of the container. Stir as far as possible. The container will receive considerable agitation when being driven to the spraying site.

2 Transport of Bulk Diluent or Mixed Herbicide from Depot to Site

The method to be adopted depends on the vehicle available. If this is a Land Rover or a tractor, it can tow a trailer. If it is a largish van, 45-gallon (205 litres) drums are the best method. Whatever the vehicle, the transporting container can be filled with the diluent by gravity from the bulk storage tank or by hose from a hydrant.

Trailers

There are a number of suitable trailers available:
M.F.R. Sales, Ltd can supply a 200-gallon (900 litres) capacity trailer which will also carry 500 lb (230 kg) of equipment.

The trailer is also suitable for fitting with a live reel sprayer. (See Chapter 13, para 6 and Plate 52).

Supplier	Description
M.F.R. Sales, Ltd c/o Camel Trailers (Bridgwater) Ltd, P.O. Box 21 Bridgwater Somerset.	Camel Liquid/Freight Trailer 200 gallon/500 lb capacity *Price* £270

A 250-gallon bowser complete with semi-rotary pump similar to that shown in Plate 65 can be obtained from:

Supplier	Description
Aldon Engineering (Yorkshire), Ltd Wortley Avenue Swinton Mexborough Yorks.	T/250 trailer fitted with semi-rotary pump suitable for pumping oil or water. *Price* £190–£230; the higher price is for a vehicle fitted with lights, etc., for road work.

An agricultural type trailer can be used for a variety of logistic purposes; a 250-gallon (1136 litre) tank measuring 3 ft 6 in (1·07 m) cube could be carried on it (Plate 66). Such tanks can be obtained from most oil distributors for about £20. The trailer could also carry spraying equipment, protective clothing, and, where necessary (e.g. with atrazine) concentrated herbicide. An alternative to the 250-gallon (1136 litre) tank is a number of 45-gallon (205 litre) drums.

Supplier	Description
Bamfords, Ltd Uttoxeter Staffs	4-ton trailer *Price* On application to manufacturers.

Persons who wish to build a trailer themselves, must observe the Motor Vehicles (Construction and Use) Regulations, 1973.

Tractor Platforms

Small platforms which fit on to a tractor's three-point linkage and which will carry 2 or 3 45-gallon (205 litre) drums are useful. The tractor can often deliver the drums right into the compartment being sprayed, thus reducing walking time. Such a trailer can be made locally (see Plates 67 and 68) or can be bought from Massey Ferguson Distributors. For the address of the local agent contact:

Supplier	Description
Massey Ferguson (UK) Ltd	M.F. 702 transporter
P.O. Box 62	*Price*
Banner Lane	£64.50
Coventry	
Warwickshire CV4 9GF.	

45-*gallon* (205 *litre*) *Drums*

In some areas, oil companies object to their drums being used other than for storing their products for a limited period and ask for quick return for cleaning and refilling. In any event, their drums should not be used for transporting diluted herbicides. Reconditioned drums can be obtained from:

Supplier	Price
Process Noble Ltd	Grade I £1.75
79–83 Coborn Road	Grade II £1.38
Bow	
London E3.	

The firm will paint the drums to the colour of your choice.

3 Storage at Site

Where the transporting vehicle is a bowser or large tank on a trailer, it is left at a convenient point on the ride and moved as necessary. 45-gallon (205 litre) drums carried on a trailer or in the back of a van can be unloaded at convenient intervals along the ride (each drum being sufficient for approximately 1 acre (0·4 of a hectare).

The use of collapsible polythene containers (see Plates 69–72), capable of holding 250 to 600 gallons (1136 to 2728 litres) of water or water-borne herbicide at intervals along the ride has been investigated. With two such tanks water could be delivered by tanker and emptied into them. When the first tank is empty, the men roll it up and carry it to the next position then start spraying from the second tank. Tanks with a 600-gallon (2728 litre) capacity complete with stack-pipe assembly and hose coupling can be obtained from:

Supplier	Description
Fertilizer Placement Ltd	600-gallon tank with stack-
Navenby	pipe assembly and coup-
Lincoln.	ling.
	Prices
	600-gallon polythene tank
	£15
	Stack-pipe assembly £3.50
	House coupling £2

These tanks are cheap compared with metal ones.

They can be made even more cheaply by local labour during wet time at a cost of about £5 for one with a capacity of 250 gallons (1136 litres). Details of manufacture are given below. These tanks are so cheap that they become consumable; they are not meant to be permanent. Whilst Fertilizer Placement Ltd say that there is no reason why this sort of tank should not be used for *storing* herbicides diluted with water or paraffin, this type of tank is particularly prone to vandalism and care should be exercised where this danger exists. If there is any possibility, e.g. of paraffin escaping from a punctured tank into a stream, other means of storage should be used. In the long term, polythene can be destroyed by light, therefore tanks should be kept in the dark when not in use.

Very similar to these "polytanks" are plastic barrel liners:

Supplier	Descriptions and Prices
Porter Lancastrian Ltd	30 gal. barrel liner with
Lancastrian Works,	1¼″ spout, 32p
Bayley St	75 gal. barrel liner with
Bolton, Lancs. BL1 3AB	1¼″ spout, 42p
	150 gal. barrel liner with
	1¼″ spout, 52p
	300 gal. barrel liner with
	¾″ spout, £1.00.

4 Constructing a 250-Gallon (1136 Litre) Polythene Storage Tank

Materials Required and Suppliers:
Polythene Tubular film on reel

Supplier	Description
Turner Whitehead	1000-gauge tubular
Industries Ltd	polythene 72 inch (180
65/71 Bermondsey Street	cm) wide, 50 yards
London SE1 3HP	(45·5 m) long.
	Price
	£15 approximately per
	reel. Note: This reel is
	sufficient to make 12
	250-gallon tanks: the
	polythene must
	measure 7 ft (2·1 m)
	long per tank.
	For extra strength
	double thickness can
	be used.

Stack-pipe and Hose Coupling

Obtained from Fertilizer Placement Ltd as above. These parts will outlive many tanks.

Wood

4 planed softwood battens 6 ft 8 in x 1½ in x 1 in (203 cm x 38 mm x 25 mm) obtainable locally.

Nuts, Bolts and Washers

48 ¼-inch B.S.W. x 2½ inches long coach bolts
48 ¼-inch B.S.W. nuts
48 ¼-inch Bright washers.

Note: Longer lengths of tubular polythene will have larger capacity, e.g. a tank 10 ft (3 m) long will hold 375 gallons (1700 litres); a 600-gallon (2728 litres) tank would be 16 ft (4·9 m) long.

Method of Construction of Tank

The method of construction is shown in Diagrams 19, 20 and 21.

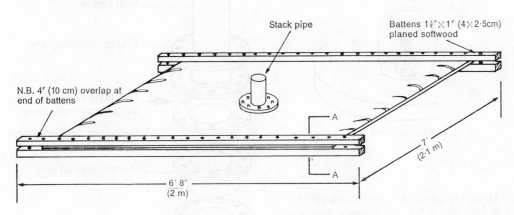

Stack pipe

Battens 1½″×1″ (4×2·5cm) planed softwood

N.B. 4″ (10 cm) overlap at end of battens

A

A

7′ (2·1 m)

6′ 8″ (2 m)

Diagram 19. Method of construction of polytank

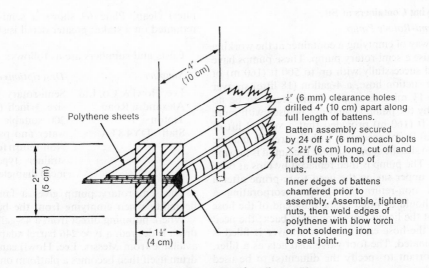

4″ (10 cm)

Polythene sheets

2″ (5 cm)

1½″ (4 cm)

¼″ (6 mm) clearance holes drilled 4″ (10 cm) apart along full length of battens.

Batten assembly secured by 24 off ¼″ (6 mm) coach bolts × 2½″ (6 cm) long, cut off and filed flush with top of nuts.

Inner edges of battens chamfered prior to assembly. Assemble, tighten nuts, then weld edges of polythene with blow torch or hot soldering iron to seal joint.

Diagram 20. Section through 'A—A' on diagram 19

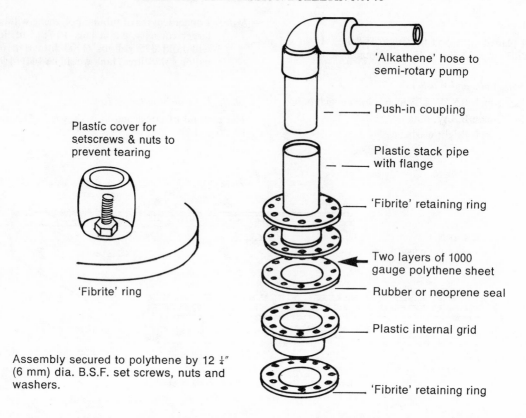

Plastic cover for
setscrews & nuts to
prevent tearing

'Fibrite' ring

Assembly secured to polythene by 12 $\frac{1}{4}$"
(6 mm) dia. B.S.F. set screws, nuts and
washers.

'Alkathene' hose to
semi-rotary pump

Push-in coupling

Plastic stack pipe
with flange

'Fibrite' retaining ring

Two layers of 1000
gauge polythene sheet

Rubber or neoprene seal

Plastic internal grid

'Fibrite' retaining ring

Diagram 21. Exploded diagram of stackpipe assembly

5   Emptying Containers at Site

Use of Semi-Rotary Pump

The best way of emptying a container at the working
site is to use a semi-rotary pump. These pumps have
been used successfully with up to 500 ft (160 m) of
alkathene suction hose, a 4-gallon (18 litre) sprayer
requiring $1\frac{1}{2}$ minutes to fill. There seems to be no
reason why the pump should not be used with more
than 500 ft (160 m) provided that a vertical lift of
20 ft (6 m) is not exceeded. In hilly areas it may be
possible to site the supply so that the liquid is flowing
downhill. The pump is then replaced by taps at both
ends, the upper saving the need to re-prime after a
move. A non-return foot-valve incorporating a
strainer should be fitted at the bulk end of the hose
to prevent the liquid from siphoning back; the need
to prime the hose each time the sprayer is filled is
thus eliminated. The foot valve also acts as a filter.
It is important to specify the diluent(s) to be used
when ordering a pump so that the manufacturers
will supply a non-corrosive model. It is essential to
keep the pump and the foot valve (especially the

filter) clean. Plate 69 shows a semi-rotary pump
mounted on a stake; greater detail is shown in Plate
73.

Costs and suppliers are as follows:

Supplier	Descriptions and Prices
Lee, Howl & Co. Ltd Alexandra Road Tipton Staffs. DY4 8TA	Semi-rotary pump No. 1 size $\frac{3}{4}$ inch (19 mm) Fig. 200 suitable for pumping water and paraffin. £7 Non-return foot valve with strainer type 3216 $(1\frac{5}{16}$ inch) diameter – £2.

The semi-rotary pump gives a fair measure of
flexibility when emptying from the bulk supply.

Where pumping direct from a 45-gallon (205 litre)
drum is desired, a type 246 barrel adaptor (Plate 74,
available from Messrs. Lee, Howl) can be used. The
drum itself then becomes a platform on which to rest
the sprayer while it is being refilled. The barrel
adaptor can of course be used for emptying the
barrel where it stands.

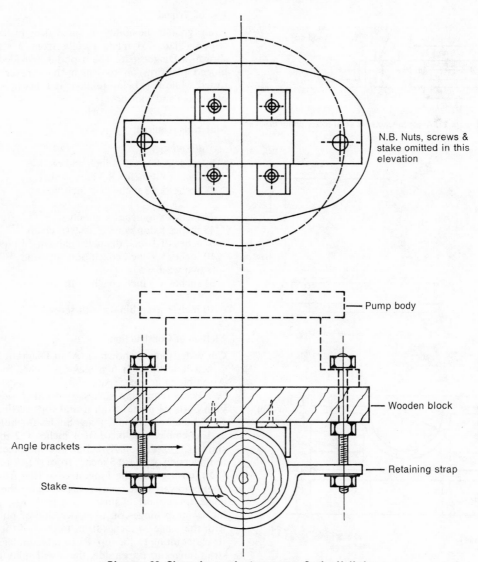

N.B. Nuts, screws &
stake omitted in this
elevation

Pump body

Wooden block

Angle brackets

Retaining strap

Stake

Diagram 22. Clamp for semi-rotary pump. Scale: Half size

More flexibility is provided by mounting the pump on to a stake in which case the bulk supply can be emptied at ride side, over a fence (at the edge of a compartment) or within the compartment itself using a length of $\frac{3}{4}$ in alkathene hose.

Mounting on the stake requires a special clamp which can be made by a blacksmith. Method of construction is shown in Diagrams 22 to 25. The following materials are required:

Material	Number
$\frac{1}{8}$ inch Angle brackets; 1 inch x 3 inches	2
Wooden block 7$\frac{1}{2}$ inch x 4$\frac{1}{2}$ inch x 1 inch	1
Retaining strap; 1$\frac{1}{4}$ inch x 1$\frac{1}{4}$ inch mild steel bar	1
7/16th inch B.S.W. stud x 3$\frac{1}{2}$ inch	2
7/16th inch B.S.W. nuts	6
7/16th inch washers	2
No. 8 wood screws x $\frac{5}{8}$ inch	4

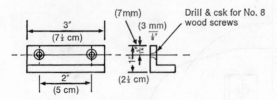

Diagram 23. Angle brackets for semi-rotary pump bracket

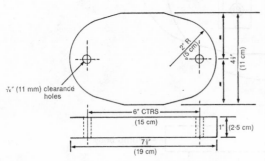

Diagram 24. Wooden block for semi-rotary pump bracket

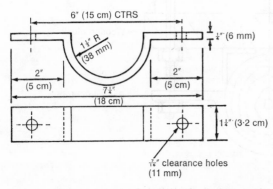

Diagram 25. Retaining strap for semi-rotary pump bracket

Ideally, the stakes should have a top diameter of 2 to 3 inches (50–75 mm) so that the retaining strap of the clamp fits snugly on to it. The wooden block of the clamp is attached to the cast iron lugs on the pump body by means of the 4 inch studs but the back of the block will have to be hollowed out slightly so that the boss at the back of the pump fits into it, allowing the block to lie flat on the pump. If a clamp cannot be made locally, one can be obtained from:

W. Denton, Automobile Engineer,
Yardley Hastings, Northampton.
The approximate cost is £2.25 plus postage.

Use of Tripod

Even greater flexibility is provided by a small tripod (Plate 75) made locally from 3 stakes as shown in Diagram 26. The tripod is provided with a hinged platform on to which the sprayer can be rested while it is being refilled. It folds up for ease of storage and transport.

Materials required

Material	Number
5 feet 6 inches x 2–3 inch stakes	3
15 inches x 4 inches x 2 inch timber	1
24 inches x 18 inches x $\frac{3}{4}$ inch board	1
or	
24 inches x 6 inches x $\frac{3}{4}$ inch	3
48 inches nylon cord or cistern chain	1
6 inches of 1-inch diameter galvanised pipe	1
10 inches x $\frac{1}{2}$ inch coach bolt, nut and two washers	1
$3\frac{1}{2}$ inches x $\frac{1}{4}$ inch coach bolt, nuts and washers	6
10 inches strap hinges with screws	2

Method of Construction

Cut water pipe as shown at 'A' in Diagram 26, drill $\frac{1}{2}$-inch hole through first stake 6 inches from top. Assemble bolt, pipe, spacers and stake as shown at 'B'. Place remaining stakes, one either side offset with butts 24 inches from it and tops resting under the 10-inch coach bolt, mark angles for holes, drill and assemble. Cut piece of 4 inches x 2 inches as shown at 'C' diagonally across the wide face, screw to underside of board 3 inches from the 18-inch edge ('D'), ensure that the longest edge (the freshly cut one) is towards the board; this will give the correct angle to support against the tripod legs. Bolt 10 inches strap hinges on to upper side of outer legs, with the hinge 24 inches from the top of the stakes, straps pointing to the top. Place table on legs, screw strap hinges to upper side, these will splay towards the edge of the table owing to the angle of the legs (a slight twist near the hinge may be needed to ensure a close fit of strap to table) lift tripod to stand square with table level. Secure nylon cord or chain to rear and front legs to prevent legs slipping apart. Bolt semi-rotary pump to rear leg with the delivery union uppermost, a short length of hose or water pipe may be fitted to this union to reach the top of the sprayers when they are placed on the table for filling and loading on to the operator's back.

6   Transporting Bulk Supplies into the Compartment

Having established a bulk supply of mixed herbicide on the ride, the next problem is to get it into the compartment to be sprayed.

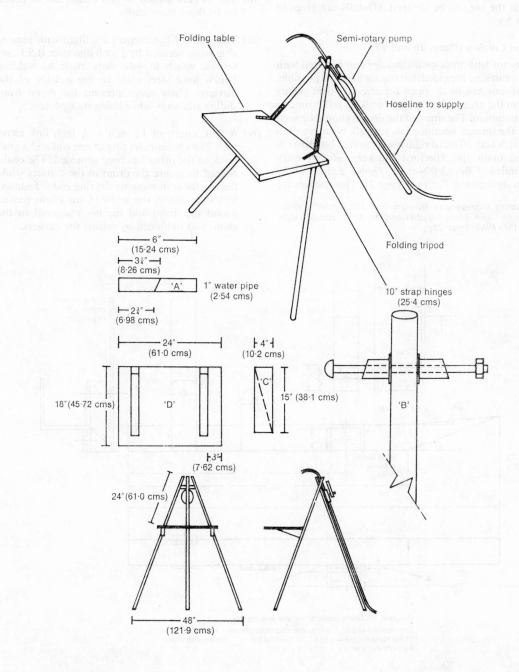

Diagram 26. Folding sprayer stand and semi-rotary pump tripod

Folding table

Semi-rotary pump

Hoseline to supply

Folding tripod

10″ strap hinges
(25·4 cms)

6″
(15·24 cms)

3¼″
(8·26 cms)

'A' 1″ water pipe
(2·54 cms)

2¾″
(6·98 cms)

24″
(61·0 cms)

4″
(10·2 cms)

18″ (45·72 cms) 'D'

'C' 15″ (38·1 cms) 'B'

3″
(7·62 cms)

24″ (61·0 cms)

48″
(121·9 cms)

Using a Semi-rotary Pump and Alkathene Hose

A bulk supply of diluted herbicide can be established on the ride in 45-gallon (205 litre) drums. The herbicide can then be pumped right into the compartment by means of a semi-rotary pump and alkathene hose, the pump being attached to a tripod inside the area to be sprayed. (Details are given in para 5.)

Drum Carriers (Plates 76 and 77)

A tractor with three-point linkage can be fitted with drum carriers. Provided that tractor access is possible, the drums can be dropped off at convenient points within the area and so reduce 'walk to refill' time to the minimum. The siting of the drums should be such that the sprayer operator has to walk no more than 30 yards (say 30 m) to refill his sprayer. The carrier is based upon the Thetford Stackers, see Forestry Commission Booklet No. 19, *Timber Extraction by Light Agricultural Tractor,** page 21. The stackers are

*Forestry Commission Booklet No. 19. *Timber Extraction by Light Agricultural Tractor* by J. W. Barraclough, HMSO 1967. Price 25p.

modified as follows to enable them to be used for carrying drums:

(i) The length is increased to 2 ft 6 in (76 cm).

(ii) The tips are angled so that drums can be rolled on to them more easily.

(iii) The sides of the carriers are fitted with removable stops secured by $\frac{3}{8}$ inch diameter B.S.F. set screws, which fit into slots made by welding $\frac{1}{4}$-inch mild steel plate to the outside of the carriers. These stops prevent the drum from sliding sideways while being transported.

(iv) A 9 ft length of $1\frac{3}{8}$ inch x $\frac{5}{16}$ inch link chain with $2\frac{1}{2}$ inch diameter ring at one end and a grab hook at the other has been provided. The chain is used to secure the drum to the carriers while the tractor is in motion; the ring end is fastened to the drawbar, the bight of the chain passed round the drum and the hook secured to the chain and tightened by raising the carriers.

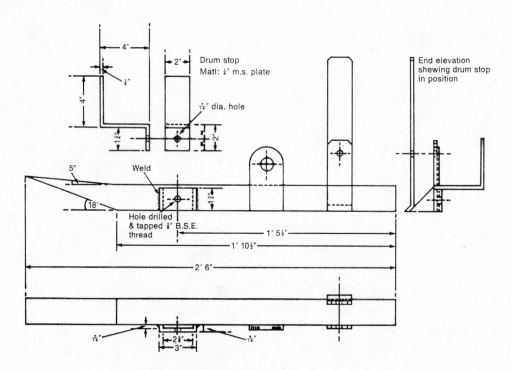

Diagram 27. Drum carriers, for use with tractor

Dimensions shown apply to the modifications only. For full details of the stackers please see F. C. Booklet No. 19, "Timber extraction by Light Agricultural Tractor" Page 21.

To enable the carriers to be built by local black-smiths or engineering firms, plans are given in Diagram 27. If in difficulty, the following supplier will be pleased to help:

Supplier	Description
J. P. Martin	Forestry Commission
Agricultural Engineers	Work Study drum carriers
Ashlow	complete with 9′ chain fit-
Mill Lane	ted with ring and grab
Hockwold	hook.
Thetford	*Price*
Norfolk	£14.50

7 Gravity Feed of Diluent to Site

Where an area to be sprayed is on a steep slope inaccessible to tractors, supply of diluted herbicide to site may be accomplished by gravity feed provided there is access along the top of the area for delivery of the herbicide mixture in 45-gallon (205 litre) drums. A Schrader self-sealing coupling is first fixed to the 2-inch (50 mm) bung from a 45-gallon (205 litre) drum. A live reel with 500 ft (150 m) of $\frac{5}{16}$ in (8 mm) bore reinforced plastic hosing is placed alongside or just below the drum which is laid on its side with the end bung close to the ground. The adaptor at the end of the connecting hose to the live reel is then inserted into the self-sealing couplings on the bung. Diluted herbicide then flows from the drum to the live reel and through the hose which is being taken down the slope to the reservoir on site. The 20-gallon (91 litre) reservoir is made of fibre glass and mounted on a stand with adjustable legs to allow for unevenness of ground when setting up (see Plate 50). It is fitted with an adaptor so that delivery commences when the hose with its self-sealing coupling is attached. The rate of delivery depends upon the vertical fall from the drum to the reservoir. A ball valve cuts off supply when the reservoir is full. Knapsack sprayers can be filled by means of a wide bore tap which gives a delivery of 3 gallon (13·6 litres) per minute with a full reservoir. Unless the hose is detached, gravity feed recommences as the reservoir is emptied. This method can also be used to convey supplies of diluent only.

The materials used were supplied as follows:

Fibre Glass Tank

Supplier	Type
Le Forte Plastics	SC 20 20-gal. fibre glass tank
New Road	fitted with bonded lid.
Newhaven	*Price*
Sussex	£7.50 plus carriage

The stand and adjustable legs were made locally at a cost of about £7.

The low pressure ball valve ($\frac{1}{2}''$ cock) and a tap cost about £2.

The total cost of the reservoir is therefore of the order of £16.

The live hose reel (Ref. No. CP. 900) can be obtained from Cooper Pegler & Co. Ltd, P.O. Box 9–151, Burgess Hill, Sussex RH15 9LA, at a cost of £22.62. This firm will also supply $\frac{5}{16}''$ bore nylon re-inforced plastic hose at 8p per foot.

Chapter 19

PROTECTION OF THE OPERATOR

1 The Pesticides Safety Precautions Scheme

Government recommendations on the safe use of herbicides (and other pesticides) are made under the Pesticides Safety Precautions Scheme (PSPS) administered by the Pesticides Branch of the Ministry of Agriculture, Fisheries and Food, Ruskin Avenue, Kew, Richmond, Surrey. Under the scheme which is voluntary, manufacturers notify the Ministry before marketing any new pesticide or suggesting a new use of an existing pesticide and put forward scientific evidence. From this, recommendations are drafted for the safe use of the pesticide. These draft recommendations go through various stages before they are finally issued as official Recommendations Sheets which are in three parts, the first part giving advice on the protection of users, the second on the protection of consumers of treated crops or foodstuffs, and the third on the protection of livestock and wild life, as well as general precautions. It is with part 1, protection of users, that this chapter is concerned. Full details of the scheme and the Recommendations Sheets can be obtained from the Ministry at the address given above.

Recommendations Sheets which relate to herbicides referred to in this book give the precautions to be taken by users as follows:

Paraquat (PSPS Recommendation Sheet No. 942 of 1.9.72)
> Wear protective gloves and face shield when handling the concentrate.
> Wash concentrate from skin or eyes immediately.
> Avoid working in spray mist.
> Wash hands and exposed skin before meals and after work.
> Remove heavily contaminated clothing immediately.

2,4,5-T (PSPS Recommendation Sheet No. 169 of 24.1.67)
> Wash concentrate from skin or eyes immediately.
> Wash hands and exposed skin before meals and after work.

2,4-D (PSPS Recommendation Sheet No. 165 of 24.1.67)
> As for 2,4,5-T.

Dalapon (PSPS Recommendation Sheet No. 405 of 1.6.68)
> Dalapon is irritating to the eyes and can be to the skin.

> Remove heavily contaminated clothing immediately.
> Wash splashes from skin or eyes immediately.
> Wash hands and exposed skin before meals and after work.

Ammonium Sulphamate: (PSPS Un-numbered Sheet dated 8.2.65)
> Wash concentrate from skin or eyes immediately.
> Avoid working in spray mist.
> Wash hands and exposed skin before meals and after work.

Dicamba: (PSPS Recommendation Sheet No. 203 of 1.2.67)
> Wash concentrate from skin or eyes immediately.
> Wash hands and exposed skin before meals and after work.

Chlorthiamid: (PSPS Recommendation Sheet No. 680 of 1.8.70)
> Wash hands before meals and after work.

Atrazine: (PSPS Recommendation Sheet No. 897 of 1.4.72)
> Wash hands before meals and after work.

Oil diluents

No sheets have been issued covering the use of oils as diluents. However, Ministry of Agriculture advisory leaflets draw attention to the risk of dermatitis if working with oil, especially diesel oil, for long periods. For this reason, it is recommended that protective gloves are used when working with 2,4,5-T in paraffin.

2 Implementation of Recommendations

None of the recommendations in paragraph 1 come within the scope of the Agriculture (Poisonous Substances) Regulations, and so cannot be enforced by processes of law. Nevertheless it is considered to be an unavoidable duty of a good employer to implement the PSPS recommendations with regard to his employees. How this is done depends on local circumstances and in particular the length of time any man will be working with a particular material. The current recommendations are tabulated and summarised in Forestry Commission Leaflet No. 51 *Chemical Control of Weeds in the Forest*, HMSO 1969. These recommendations are considered so important that no apology is made for repeating them here.

The recommendations for protective clothing are given in Table 10. They are made on the assumptions:

(i) that workers concerned are likely to remain on such work for several days at a time;

(ii) that the vegetation sprayed at medium volume rates is likely to be treated by knapsack and lance operating at low pressure and spraying at up to knee-height. In such circumstances spray solution can be transferred back to the operator as he walks; hence the need for oil-proof (and water-proof) trousers and boots. Paraquat is sprayed on to grasses not more than 9 inches (23 cms) tall and water-proof trousers are not essential if Wellington boots are worn;

(iii) that low-volume sprays are applied by aircraft or mistblower, and droplets are likely to cover the vegetation at least up to waist height and sometimes higher. In gusty winds, occasional swirls of droplets may envelop the operator. These can, and should, be minimised by working so that the spray blast is directed down wind from the position of the operator;

(iv) the equipment is maintained in good order with a well fitting leak-proof filling lid and joints that do not leak, and that care is taken in filling not to get spray solution outside the container, wiping off splashes that may run down and drip on to the operator;

(v) finally, while for operations such as handling concentrates, protective clothing is obligatory for the safety or well-being of the operator, for other operations it is intended to reduce the risk of discomfort. As some of the protective clothing can itself be uncomfortable – for example on difficult terrain in hot weather, it is important to distinguish between what is essential and what must be worn in all conditions, and what a supervisor may allow to be taken off at his discretion. Table 10 is laid out with this distinction in mind.

For all compounds, the PSPS Recommendations Sheets lay down that splashes of any concentrate must be washed from the skin or eyes immediately. It follows that if concentrates are to be handled in the forest, washing water must be taken there too. If this is impracticable, goggles must be worn to protect the eyes and a waterless skin cleanser and paper towels must be instantly available.

It is also stated that in all circumstances workers should wash before meals and after work. Soap and water must be available at such times, or a waterless skin cleanser and paper towels.

Respirators are mentioned in Table 10 because some workers have experienced discomfort when working with paraffin for long periods. The require-

ment "avoid working in spray mist" for paraquat and ammonium sulphamate can also be met, as far as the nose and mouth is concerned, by wearing a respirator capable of filtering out all fine droplets. However, it should not be necessary to create a spray mist; these two materials should be applied to low-growing vegetation by knapsack sprayer operating at 10 lbs per sq inch pressure ($0.7 \, kg/cm^2$) or less. Ammonium sulphamate solution may be applied to frills from a container emptying solely by gravity. By keeping the spray nozzle down, working at low pressure, and keeping upwind of the spray nozzle, operators run no risk of working in a spray mist.

The requirement of a face shield when handling paraquat concentrate can be met by using goggles such as are listed in para 9, provided means are instantly to hand to wipe off splashes from skin of the face and mouth. Otherwise a face shield should be worn.

The requirement to wear gloves when handling paraquat concentrate can be met by use of heavy PVC gloves. Such gloves are also suitable when working with 2,4,5-T in paraffin. Thin rubber, unlined gloves are too easily torn to make them a practical proposition when using herbicides in forest operations. However, it is vital that the lined gloves recommended are examined regularly and frequently to see that they are sound and clean. They achieve the exact opposite of what is intended if the lining absorbes any herbicide and holds it against the operator's skin. Another alternative is thin polythene gloves which are used once and then thrown away.

Barrier cream rubbed into the skin, hands and wrists reduces the risk of dermatitis and is recommended when using paraffin for long periods, especially by operators whose skin is easily inflamed.

3 Requirements of the Law

Interpretation of the law is never straightforward and that relating to protective clothing and safety measures generally is no exception. The Scottish Forestry Productivity Committee have obtained legal opinion which has been published as an Appendix to their Pamphlet No. 17. This is considered to be of such importance that permission has been obtained to reproduce it below:

"*Safety Measures for Forest Workers*
The following opinion on the general responsibility of employers for the safety of forestry and agricultural workers has been obtained from the Scottish Woodland Owners Association's law agents, Messrs Henderson and Jackson, Writers to the Signet:

QUID JURIS?
(1) The law imposes upon the employer of agricultural and forestry workers an obligation to take

TABLE 10

PROTECTIVE CLOTHING WHEN USING HERBICIDES IN THE FOREST

Clothing	Ammonium sulphamate			Atrazine and dalapon in water		Paraquat in water	Asulam, dicamba 2,4,5-T, 2,4-D and 2,4,5-T/2,4-D mixtures in water		2,4,5-T in paraffin		2,4,5-T/2,4-D ULV formulations	Chlorthiamid Dichlobenil
	Crystals	Medium Volume	Low Volume	Medium Volume	Low Volume	Medium Volume	Medium Volume	Low Volume	Medium Volume	Low Volume	Ultra low Volume	Granules
Boots Wellington Rubber or oil resistant	D	E	E	E	E	E	E	E	E	E Note (4)	E Note (4)	D
Trousers Waterproof or Leggings *Notes* (1) & (7)	D	E	E	E	E	E	E	E	E	E Note (4)	—	—
Jacket Waterproof *Note* (7)	—	D	E	D	E	D	D	E	D/E	E Note (4) and (5)	—	—
Gloves Plastic	E	E	E	E	E	E	E	E	E	E	E	D/E Note (8)
Face Shield or Eye Shield	—	—	D	—	D	D/E Note (2)	—	E	D	E	E	—
Respirator Note (3)	—	—	D	—	D	—	—	D	D	D	D	D Note (8)
Hat or Hood Waterproof or oilproof	—	—	D	—	D	—	—	D/E Note (6)	D	D/E Note (4) and (6)	E (4)	—
Ultra Low Volume Suit	—	—	—	—	—	—	—	—	—	—	E	—

Notes on Table 10

The rates of application of herbicides in medium, low, and ultra low volume spraying are given in Table 7, page 29.

E = essential: laid down under Pesticides Safety Precautions Scheme or considered necessary in relation to working conditions in forestry.

D = discretionary: must be available. Such items may reduce discomfort and so should be made freely available, although the final choice should rest with the operator.

(1) Waterproof trousers are very uncomfortable to wear due to condensation and heat retention. Risk of contamination from the spray may be more comfortably avoided by wearing waterproof leggings.

(2) Face shield essential when handling concentrate but not otherwise.

(3) For sprays in water a respirator designed to intercept droplets is adequate. For sprays in oil, if the smell causes discomfort, a respirator designed to intercept vapour as well as droplets can be used. Special masks are available for ultra low volume spraying – see Chapter 17, para 14.

(4) The material used for boots or protective clothing needs to be oilproof. Rubber is not oilproof.

(5) A jacket is essential when using a knapsack sprayer.

(6) A hat or hood is essential for groundmarkers during aerial spraying.

(7) In some circumstances, this clothing may also need to be thornproof.

(8) Paper face mask and gloves may be desired when filling applicator.

reasonable care for their safety. Accidents in the abstract cannot unfortunately be prevented by any standard of care however high, but the law in deciding whether the employer is to blame either wholly or in part for a particular accident which happens will ask whether the employer exercised the care, having regard to all the circumstances, which a prudent and careful employer in his position would have done and whether the accident that did in fact occur was one which might reasonably have been foreseen. This obligation is one at common law and in a sense requires the accident to happen before the decision can be taken about who is to blame.

(2) The principal common law obligations of all employers are (a) to provide a competent staff – this means in practice that all employees should be suitably trained for the job in hand; (b) to provide suitable materials and to see that the materials are regularly inspected and kept in good order and condition; and (c) to ensure that a proper and safe system of working is regularly carried out; this means that on any given task a tested and approved method should be employed and that a sufficient number of men should be allocated to each particular job, e.g. an employer would be liable in damages if one man were asked to carry out an operation which in the ordinary way could only be safely carried out by two or more men and an accident occurred.

(3) There are in addition a number of leading statutes which lay down the safety measures which an employer must take and which determine his liability in the event of his failure to take these steps. Of these the Agriculture (Safety, Health and Welfare Provisions) Act 1956 the Occupiers Liability (Scotand) Act 1960 and the Factories Act 1961 require special consideration. From these Acts flow the strict rules and regulations dealing with almost every aspect of the safety, health and welfare of employees in the course of their employment and the test of their reasonableness or otherwise does not apply; they are rules of strict liability which an employer ignores or fails to abide by at his peril. It is imperative not only that employers should be familiar with the broad outline of their terms, but should also keep up to date with the many statutory rules and regulations which have been made under and subsequent to the coming into force of these Acts. Information as to what these regulations are is readily available from H.M.S.O. Approximately fourteen such regulations have already been under the Agriculture (Safety, Health and Welfare Provisions) Act 1956, which deal principally with the provision of first aid equipment, the use of portable ladders, the avoidance of accidents to children, the provision of safe work places, the lifting of heavy weights, the guarding of stationary machinery and of power take-offs on tractors and the guarding of circular saws.

(4) These legal considerations are, however, no substitute for common sense, and it cannot be too strongly emphasised that it is the duty of employers to take the greatest care and consideration for the safety and well-being of their employees. Many employees are naturally of a careless and happy-go-lucky disposition, but this only means that an employer must insist with the greatest firmness that employees make proper use of all safety devices designed for their protection and that they avoid short cuts which involve them in dangerous situations. There is in short no substitute for regular supervision and inspection of the men employed and their methods of working and where employers cannot personally undertake such supervision they must see to it that competent and experienced servants undertake that work for them."

4 Protective Clothing

Each of the types of clothing listed in Table 10 is now examined in turn. Specific recommendations for ultra low volume spraying are given in Chapter 17, para 14, page 59.

5 Jackets and Trousers

The specification that a suit should be oil-proof (and hence water-proof), thornproof, ventilated and reasonably warm is a difficult one. In practice, such a suit is bound to be expensive; the following are suggested:

For Oil-borne Sprays
Jalite's All-purpose Polyurethane Suit (green)

Supplier:	*Descriptions and Prices:*	
Abridge Overalls Ltd	Jacket	£4.17
Burgess Hill	Trousers	£2.50
Sussex	Leggings	£1.57
	Sizes available:	
	Small, medium, large and extra large.	

For Water-borne Sprays in thorny conditions
Polymac Suit (green) with or without pockets

Supplier:	*Prices:*
Write in first instance to:	Please consult manufacturers
	Sizes available:
Watsons (Newburgh) Ltd	Small, medium and large.
Newburgh	
Fife	

F

For wet conditions, but little likelihood of tearing
Northylon NCN 106

Supplier:	Descriptions and Prices:
James North & Son Ltd P.O. Box 3 Hyde Cheshire	Jackets, long coats, trousers and leggings are available in a range of sizes. Jackets cost approx. £1.75 and trousers about £1.34.

6 Wellington Boots (oil-proof)

The boots listed are knee-length and lined. Unlined boots are not recommended as they are too easily pierced by sharp objects such as cut coppice.

Supplier:	Details:
Clark, Hoy & Co., Ltd.	Dunlop "Challenger"
Fen Street,	Sizes:
Canning Town,	6–12
London E16 1JT	Price
	£2.38

7 Headwear

The only mandatory requirement of headwear is for ground markers during aerial spraying though a hat can be worn when mistblowing. A sou'wester is probably the best type of headwear.

Supplier:	Description:
James North & Sons Ltd P.O. Box 3 Hyde Cheshire	Sou'wester type FWNS Sizes: Small, medium and large. Price 36p
Also available from:	

Supplier:	Description:
Abridge Overalls Ltd Burgess Hill Sussex	Sou'wester black or yellow PVC or "Handikap". Price 35p

8 Gloves

The ideal glove would be unlined but in practice such gloves tend to retain perspiration and rapidly become uncomfortable. They also tend to tear easily. In practice, the use of unlined gloves should be restricted to handling concentrates at a depot where bulk pre-mixing is practiced. The most useful type of glove for this work is the disposable polythene glove:

Supplier:	Description:
The Polythene Glove Co. Rydal House Copse Road Fleetwood Lancs. FY7 6RP	Disposable polythene glove. Sizes: Medium and large. Price £4.13 per 1000 Medium or Large.

An alternative is to use a lined glove in conjunction with a barrier cream. The danger with using lined gloves is that if drops of concentrated herbicide or oil fall on the lining they are held in contact with the skin and can cause dermatitis. Hence their use (with barrier cream) should be restricted to the application of pre-mixed herbicides. The following type is used by the Forestry Commission:

Supplier:	Description:
James North & Son Ltd P.O. Box 3 Hyde Cheshire	No. 540 Plastochrome glove Length: 12″ Sizes: 6½, 7½, 8½, 9½. Price 28p per pair.

A suitable barrier cream is Rozalex No. 10.

Supplier:	Description:	
Rozalex Ltd Road One Industrial Estate Winsford Cheshire	Rozalex No. 10 barrier cream. Price	
	16 oz	47p.
	5 litre	£2.56.
	15 ,,	£6.83.

Barrier cream can of course be used on the face and neck, as well as the hands and wrists.

9 Goggles and Face Shields

Face shields must be worn when neat herbicides such as paraquat and dicamba are being handled. It is Forestry Commission policy to make goggles available to workers who request them during spraying operations.

Supplier:	Description:
Face Shield Safety Products Ltd Holmthorpe Avenue Redhill Surrey.	Clearways face shield Price £1.00 approximately.

Supplier:	Description:
Goggles Pyrene Panorama Ltd Hanworth Air Park Feltham Middx.	Panoramette chemical goggle (Transparent PVC frame with gauze filter ventilation. Wide cellulose acetate window.) Prices 42p each with reduction for bulk orders. Spare windows 11p each.

Note: These goggles are not suitable for wear with the respirators listed in para 10. There is no really suitable goggle for this purpose; perhaps the most acceptable are the cheap disposable eye shields listed below:

Supplier:	Description:
Industrial Glove Co. Ltd Nailsea Somerset BS19 2BX	Eye-shield type 6638 (non-inflammable eye-shield with leather bound edges).
	Price 29p.

Goggles sometimes mist up. This can be prevented by applying car anti-mist fluid (small bottles available from Boots at about 20p), by rubbing a tiny amount of soap on to the inside of the window, or by the use of a proprietary anti-mist cloth.

10 Respirators (See Plates 78 and 79)

It should be noted that none of the herbicides listed in para 1 of this chapter require the use of a respirator. Sometimes however a worker will express a desire to be issued with one and sometimes it is not possible for him to avoid working in spray mist as when marking for aerial spraying. The following recommendations (which are under review at the time of writing) allow for two main sets of circumstances:

(i) Where vapour is rising from the ground or from foliage as for example on a hot day when 2,4,5-T in paraffin is being applied;

(ii) Where no such vapour is present and the respirator is required only to intercept droplets created by the sprayer.

Where vapour due to evaporation is present:
Toxigard Agricultural Respirator (BS 2577)

Supplier:	Description:
Matty & Co Ltd Mattay House 2 Highr Road Liverpool L25 0QQ	Toxigard Agricultural Respirator Type QR 3086, fitted with two RC 86 cartridges.
also at:	*Price*
17 Dundee Road Slough Trading Estate Slough, Bucks SL1 4JU	Respirator £3.30 complete. Spare RC 86 cartridges, 48p.

Where no vapour caused by evaporation is present:
Baxter Pneu-Seal Dust Respirator (BS 2091)

Manufacturers:	Description:
The Leyland & Birmingham Rubber Co Ltd. Leyland Preston Lancs PR5 1UP distributed by: Sabre Safety Ltd 225 Ash Road Aldershot Hants.	Pneu-seal dust mask with dust cartridge. *Price* £1.95 Pre-filter pads should be used with these masks and cost 50p per 100.

These masks have a pneumatic rim and hence mould to the user's face. Replacement filters, called "Encapsulated resin wool fine filters", cost 19p each. It is important that respirators be cleaned regularly with warm water and a mild detergent such as Fairy liquid and sterilised with a disinfectant such as a solution of Dettol, TCP or Savlon. Filters must be replaced after 8 hours in use.

11 Washing Facilities

While soap and towel are the best means of washing, where clean water is not readily available an alternative is a waterless hand cleanser used with paper towels.

Supplier:	Description:		
Rozalex, Ltd Road One Industrial Estate Winsford Cheshire	Waterless Skin Cleanser No 44		
	Ref No	*Weight*	*Price*
	1139	75 gm tube	£2.40 per doz
	1141	16 oz tin	£0.27 each
	1144	5 litre	£1.48 each
	1145	15 „	£4.30 each
	1146	30 „	£8.41 each
	1147	50 „	£12.10 each

Paper towels are available as follows:

Supplier:	Price
Jeyes U.K. Ltd Brunel Way Thetford Norfolk.	5 cases each containing 18 packs of 200 towels cost £2.94 per case.

A dispenser is available on free loan.

12 Publications

Certain publications dealing with safety aspects of chemical spraying are available as shown below:

Free of charge from:

Ministry of Agriculture, Fisheries & Food, Whitehall Place, London SW1, and the Department of Agriculture & Fisheries for Scotland, Chesser House, Gorgie Road, Edinburgh EH11 3AW:—

The Safe Use of Poisonous Chemicals on the Farm (Leaflet APS/1)

Code of Practice for Ground Spraying

Poisoning by Pesticides – First Aid Measures (Leaflet APS/3)

Do's and Don'ts for Users of Chemical Sprays

Dermatitis among Land Workers

To all Operators of Spraying Machines.

From: The Joint A.B.M.A.C./Wild Life Education and Communications Committee, Alembic House, Albert Embankment, London SE1:

Pesticides – A Code of Conduct, price 5p.

Free of charge from:

The Industrial Technical Service Division of Alexander Duckham & Co. Ltd, Summit House, West Wickham, Kent, BR4 0SJ:

The Causes and Prevention of Industrial Dermatitis.

13   British Standards

The British Standards listed below have a relevance to the protection of the operator in the application of herbicides and can be obtained from:

> The British Standards Institution
> Sales Branch
> 101/113 Pentonville Road
> London N1.

A Sectional list of British Standards dealing with personal safety equipment (ref No: SL 30) is also available.

Ref Number	Title
BS 1651: 1966	Industrial Gloves
BS 1870: Part 2: 1961	Safety Footwear Part 2, Rubber safety boots
Part 3: 1966	Safety Footwear Part 3, Lined moulded rubber safety boots
BS 2091: 1969	Respirators for Protection against harmful dusts and gases
BS 2092: 1967	Industrial Eye Protectors
BS 2577: 1955	Methylene Blue Particulate test for Respirator Canisters
BS 2617: 1965	Respirators for Agricultural Workers using Toxic chemicals
BS 4555: 1970	High Efficiency Dust respirators.

PART E
OTHER METHODS OF WEEDING

Chapter 20

THE USE OF BLACK POLYTHENE AS A WEED SUPPRESSOR

1 Introduction

There are a number of possible alternatives to hand, machine and chemical weeding as described in Parts B, C and D of this Bulletin but the only one studied by the Work Study Branch of the Forestry Commission and meriting inclusion is the use of black polythene as a weed suppressor. Because of the high cost of hand weeding (the main method then) a small trial was laid down in 1966 to test the effectiveness of black polythene when used as a weed suppressor. It was felt that in conditions where, for example, mature oak had been clear felled and the ground was temporarily free from all weed growth, black polythene placed around the new tree would help to maintain the ground in its immediate vicinity free from competing weed growth. (See Plate 80.)

2 Trials and the Reasons for Doing Them

The trials were designed to determine:

(1) the degree of suppression of various weed types

(2) the effect on the growth of the trees

(3) the length of time the polythene lasted

(4) the effectiveness of the method of securing the polythene.

3 Sites and Treatments

Ten plots were laid down at Hazelborough Forest (Northants) and Lavenham Forest (Essex). Both forests are on heavy clay and both are problem weed areas. Each of the ten plots was subdivided at random into 3 treatments:

(i) Polythene with no weeding.

(ii) Polythene with hand weeding between the squares.

(iii) Control – no polythene. Weeded in the same manner as the rest of the compartment.

Each tree was surrounded by a square of 150 gauge black polythene sheeting 36 in x 36 in (0·9 m x 0·9 m). At the corners, fencing wire staples 6 in x 6 in x 6 in (15 cm x 15 cm x 15 cm) were used to hold the square down. To minimise tearing, the corners of the polythene squares were folded so that four

layers were pierced. The staples were made from old fencing wire by forest labour in wet time. Tree heights were measured immediately after the polythene had been applied and also after the end of each growing season. Missing or dead trees were noted. Degree of colonisation by weed species was also recorded.

4 Results of Trials

Pre-trial costing indicated that, to be successful, the polythene would have to be effective for 3 years. In practice none of the polythene squares was moved or disturbed by the weeds in that period. In fact most of the polythene was still there after five years. Weed suppression in general was good. There was some indication of small holes having been made by children but this was not sufficient to affect the results. Statistical analysis showed that there was no significant difference in the growth rate of the trees in any of the three treatments. In other words, the presence of the polythene was not detrimental to the tree growth. Similarly there was no significant difference in the number of deaths occurring in any of the three treatments. There was no sign of the polythene breaking down or tearing from the staples. The wire staple system of securing the polythene was effective and simple. The main weed species encroaching upon the trees were climbers, especially bramble, but they were not able to penetrate the polythene. By the end of the second growing season the bramble was growing over the black polythene and in some cases over the trees themselves. No other weed species gave any trouble.

5 Conclusions

In 1965, hand weeding in the heavy clay forests of Northamptonshire and Essex was costing up to £15 per acre per annum (£37 per hectare), including labour oncost, for two weedings a year. Weeding was frequently necessary for three years or more. Assuming a weeding period of 3 years, the total cost by hand was therefore £45 per acre (£111 per hectare). The cost of polythene and applying it was £36 per acre (£89 per hectare). The minimum saving on hand weeding over the three-year period was therefore of the order of £9 per acre (£22 per hectare) or 20 per cent. Since 1965 however, chemical weeding has made a considerable impact and three years application of paraquat (at two applications per annum) would cost only about £21 per acre (£52 per hectare) for labour, labour oncost and chemicals at the same rates as in the previous calculations. One can only conclude therefore that this experiment though successful was overtaken by events and economically black polythene as a weed suppressor can not be justified as an alternative to chemical. It is however an extremely useful alternative to bear in mind in circumstances where chemicals or machines cannot be used. Persons interested in trying the technique for themselves can obtain suitable 150 gauge black polythene from:

Turner Whitehead Industries Ltd
65/71 Bermondsey Street
London SE1 3HP.

PART F
COSTING THE OPERATION AND CHOOSING
THE METHOD

Chapter 21

COSTS

1 General

Costs given in this chapter are based on the principles outlined in paras 2–9 except where some other basis (which is clearly stated) has had to be used. The figures may not apply to conditions outside the Forestry Commission (or indeed in specific areas within the Commission) but it is not difficult to substitute different factors such as other rates of pay, other incentive levels and other overhead charges, to arrive at meaningful costs.

2 Labour Charges

The two grades of worker mainly involved in weeding operations have been charged at the weekly wage rate in force in the Forestry Commission on "Decimalisation Day", 15th February 1971. These are:

Grade of Worker	Weekly rate of pay*
Skilled Forest Worker	£15.68
Wheeled tractor driver	£15.95
(after 6 months)	

3 Incentive Levels

The Forestry Commission has agreed with the Trade Unions that its piecework rates shall be such that a skilled forest worker shall be able to earn a minimum of 30% above day pay while he is employed on piecework. This factor has been used with hand weeding operations. Though it is not part of the Forestry Commission's agreement, the calculations here allow an extra 10% incentive where machines or chemicals are used. Hence the calculations are based on the following incentive levels:

Hand work – 30% incentive.
Work involving Machines or Chemicals – 40% incentive.

4 Labour Oncost

Labour oncost (LO) consists of charges which are

payable when a man is employed, e.g. national insurance, holidays, sick leave, wet time when no work can be done, transport of workers, training and provision for pensions and gratuities. In the Forestry Commission, if one assumes an average working year for a worker of 200 days, this amounted (in 1971) to £1.80 per day.

5 Machine Costs

Rather than use historical costs which vary between machines of the same class and also between areas, a standard formula to give more uniform rates has been used. This formula is:

$$\text{Hourly cost of the machine (excluding driver, etc.)} = \frac{\text{Capital Cost} \times 3}{\text{Estimated life in hours}}$$

Unless otherwise stated, a life of 8000 hours (i.e. 5 years x 1600 hours or 8 years x 1000 hours) has been used.

6 Cost of Materials

Cost of chemicals, paraffin and other materials are charged at rates applicable in mid 1971. Reduced rates for purchases in bulk have been used where they are available.

7 Rates of Application of Herbicides

Unless otherwise stated, calculations are based on the dilution rates and rates of application shown in Table 5.

8 Other Factors

Unless otherwise stated, a spacing of 2·1 m x 2·1 m (approximately 7′ x 7′) has been assumed giving 2268 trees per hectare (918 trees per acre). It is impossible in a work of this kind to cost all possible alternatives, but a reader who has familiarised himself with the standard timetables and output guides will readily be able to calculate costs for his own conditions.

---

*On 1st April 1973 these rates were £19.28 and £19.48 respectively.

9　Prices per Standard Minute

The method of calculating prices per standard minute is given in Appendix I para 6. For the two grades of workers usually employed on weeding work, and based on the principles given in para 3, these prices are:

Grade of Worker	Incentive level	
	30%	40%
Skilled Forest Worker	0.85p	0.91p
Wheeled Tractor Driver	0.86p	0.93p

Labour oncost, machine costs and material costs too can be expressed as a price per minute. With labour oncost, the £1.80 per day (see para 4) when divided by 480 minutes (8 hours x 60 minutes) gives a price per minute of 0.38p. With the machine formula (see para 5), providing the estimated life is 8000 hours, each £1000 of capital value produces an hourly rate of 37.5p which can be expressed as a price per minute of 0.62p.

10　The Cost of the Job

Where standard timetables or output guides are available, the cost of the job is made up as follows:

(i) *Labour*　Standard time x price per standard minute (p/SM) for worker at appropriate incentive level.

(ii) *Labour Oncost*　Standard time x 0.38p

(iii) *Machine Cost*

$$\text{Standard time x } \frac{\text{Capital Cost}}{1000} \text{ x 0.62p}$$

(iv) *Chemicals, diluent, etc.*　Standard time x actual cost per minute of materials used.

Unless made clear in the text, costs given are based on this system.

11　Cost of Hand Weeding

The costs shown in Table 11 are based on the times given in standard timetable No XV/1 in Appendix II. Readers would be advised to familiarise themselves with that table and in particular with the system of classifying weed growth into four groups each with three grades of difficulty explained in paragraph 5 and the Appendix of that table.

This table assumes one season's weed growth only and applies to an average season.

12　Job Specification

These costs are for carrying out the work described in the Job Specification (para 2) of the Standard Time Booklet. This states:

"To cut a swath 1 metre wide leaving the stubble 15–23 cms high between the plants and 8–15 cms high around them. Inter-row vegetation is to be topped only if it is high enough or likely to become high enough to fall on the trees. Cut vegetation is to be kept clear of major drains, footpaths and rides."

13　Variations to the Specification

If this specification is varied, the work content will be greater or less. The reader will therefore be able to estimate for himself the likely effect on the cost. Increases to the costs can also arise from the factors listed in paragraph 7 of the Standard Time Table.

14　Example

Taking an example of weed growth; an assessment of a typical compartment to be weeded has shown the growth to consists of 50% average herbaceous plants, 10% moderate climbers and 40% moderate woody weeds in 2·1 m row spacing. Using Table 11, a reasonable estimate of the cost would be as follows:

$$50\% \text{ average herbaceous plants } = \frac{£6.9 + £20.1}{2} \text{ x } \cdot5 = £6.7$$

$$10\% \text{ moderate climbers } = \frac{£14.6 + £30.7}{2} \text{ x } \cdot1 = £2.3$$

$$40\% \text{ moderate woody weeds } = \frac{£17.4 + £41.2}{2} \text{ x } \cdot4 = £11.7$$

Therefore reasonable estimate of cost of weeding 1 hectare　= £20·7

TABLE 11

WEEDING BY HAND

Weed Type	Labour (£/hectare)	Labour Oncost (£/hectare)	Total Cost (£/hectare)
Group A weeds (Herbs, bracken, soft grasses)	4·8–13·9	2·1–6·2	6·9–20·1
Group B weeds (Coarse grasses, rushes)	7·6–17·6	3·4–7·9	11·0–25·5
Group C weeds (Climbers including bramble)	10·1–21·2	4·5–9·5	14·6–30·7
Group D weeds (Woody weeds)	12·0–28·5	5·4–12·7	17·4–41·2

Colour Plate 1. After one pass of a rotating bar weeding machine powered by a narrow gauge tractor, the relief given to the crop trees in a 1·5 m spaced plantation can be clearly seen.

Colour Plate 2. *Calamagrostis epigeios* at Hazelborough Forest, Northants. It is one of the most difficult grasses to control.

Colour Plate 3. Nozzles

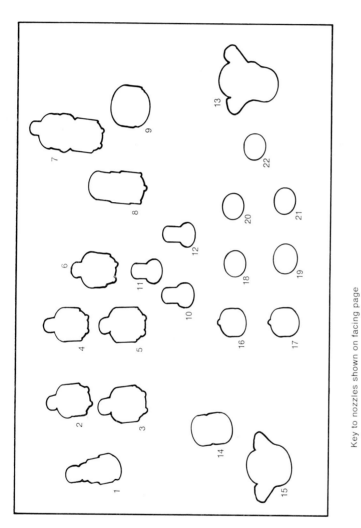

Key to nozzles shown on facing page

1   PP 78 brass floodjet (same as Nos 2, 3, 7 and 10)
2, 3   Red Polijets (78) (same as Nos 1, 7 and 10)
4, 5   Blue Polijets (62) (same as No 11)
6   Yellow Polijet (40) (same as No 12)
7   Red Politip with nozzle cap and holder (same as Nos 1, 2, 3 and 10)
8   Politip holder
9   Politip nozzle cap
10   Red Politip (78) (same as Nos 1, 2, 3 and 7)
11   Blue Politip (62) (same as Nos 4 and 5)
12   Yellow Politip (40) (same as No 6)
13   No 520 nozzle with stainless steel disc
14, 15 No 520 nozzle dismantled
16, 17 Swirlers for use with No 520 nozzle
18, 19 Ceramic discs for use with No 520 nozzle
20, 21 Stainless steel discs for use with No 520 nozzle (No 21 is a five hole rose jet)
22   Brass hollow cone nozzle for use with No 520 nozzle and Politec guard
Note: Politips can also be used with No 520 nozzle.

Colour Plates 4 and 5 *above* and *below:* Fifteen year old Norway spruce at Wicken Wood, Hazelborough Forest, Northants, *before* and *after* having been given a foliar application of 2,4,5-T diluted with water.

15 Cost of Chemical Weeding

It is perhaps easiest to look at the various problems which arise and which can be solved by using chemical techniques. Only current, well-tested methods are costed here.

16 Treatment of Grass and Herbaceous Weeds

There are three main methods:

Spot treatment using dalapon or paraquat applied by a knapsack sprayer fitted with a guard to protect the tree.

Strip or spot treatment using atrazine applied by a knapsack sprayer with no guard.

Strip or spot treatment using the granular weed killer chlorthiamid (Prefix) using the Horstine Farmery motorised granule applicator.

These methods are examined in turn.

(i) Paraquat/Dalapon (Output Guide XV/G5)

Each tree will be sprayed with 42 cc's of diluted herbicide, a total of 95·2 litres per gross hectare. With a dilution rate of 6 litres of paraquat in 350 litres of water, 1·6 litres of paraquat will be used and 93·6 litres of water. If the herbicide is dalapon, the same volume (95·2 litres) will be applied but 3·3 kg of dalapon will be used.

TABLE 12

SPOT APPLICATION OF PARAQUAT OR DALAPON BY KNAPSACK SPRAYER

Treatment	Labour (£/ha)	Labour Oncost (£/ha)	Chemicals (£/ha)	Total Cost (£/ha)
Paraquat	3·62	1·51	2·29	7·42
Dalapon	3·62	1·51	1·29	6·42

Note: Conveying water to the site would increase these costs by about £0.25 per hectare.

(ii) Atrazine used as a wettable powder (Output Guide XV/G3)

With spot application, an area of 1 sq m around each tree (22·7% of the total area) will be sprayed. If band spraying is used, 1 m bands (47.6% of the total area) will be sprayed. *The costs in Table 3 are based on 9 kg of atrazine in 450 litres of water per treated hectare.*

TABLE 13

APPLICATION OF ATRAZINE BY KNAPSACK SPRAYER

Treatment	Labour (£/ha)	Labour Oncost (£/ha)	Chemicals (£/ha)	Total Cost (£/ha)
Band	2·48	1·03	4·54	8·05
Spot	1·85	0·77	2·17	4·79

Carriage of water is additional, reasonable charges per treated hectare being £0.25 for spot treatment and £0.45 for band treatment.

(iii) Chlorthiamid used as a granule (Output Guide XV/G4)

The output guide gives outputs for band and spot treatment. With band treatment, the specification is to treat strips 1 m wide, hence if the trees are planted in rows 2·1 m apart, about half the gross area will be treated. Similarly with spot treatment, the specification is to treat half the row, therefore, with a spacing of 2·1 m x 2·1 m, one quarter of the total area will be treated. The same proportions apply to the quantity of chemical used; 60 kg of chlorthiamid should be applied to a gross hectare, hence 30 kg will be applied in band treatment and 15 kg in spot treatment. The knapsack applicator is charged at 12½p per hour.

TABLE 14

APPLICATION OF CHLORTHIAMID (PREFIX) USING HORSTINE FARMERY MOTORISED KNAPSACK APPLICATOR

Treatment	Labour (£/ha)	Labour Oncost (£/ha)	Chemicals (£/ha)	Machine (£/ha)	Total Cost (£/ha)
Band	1·54	0·64	13·80	0·36	16·34
Spot	1·42	0·59	6·90	0·33	9·24

The table assumes a distance to refill point averaging 50 metres.

17 Summary of Costs of Weeding in Grass and Herbaceous Weeds

TABLE 15

SUMMARY OF COSTS OF WEEDING IN GRASS AND HERBACEOUS WEEDS

Treatment	Cost per ha including haulage of diluent
Paraquat	£7·7
Dalapon	£6·7
Atrazine – Band	£8·5
– Spot	£5·0
Chlorthiamid – Band	£16·3
– Spot	£9·2

18 Foliage Treatment of Woody Weeds

The main herbicide for this type of work is 50% 2,4,5-T emulsifiable ester diluted with water. There are a number of ways of applying it:

Knapsack sprayers
Knapsack Mistblowers
Tractor mounted Mistblowers
Aircraft.

These are examined in turn:

(i) Knapsack Sprayers (Output Guide XV/G6)
The recommended dilution rate is 4·5–7 litres in herbicide in 350–700 litres of water per treated hectare. The costs in Table 16 are based on this range of application rates.

TABLE 16

APPLICATION OF 2,4,5-T IN WATER TO FOLIAGE
USING A KNAPSACK SPRAYER

Rate of Dilution	Labour (£/ha)	Labour Oncost (£/ha)	Herbicide (£/ha)	Total Cost (£/ha)
4·5 litres in 350 litres of water	3·23	1·35	2·70	7·28
7 litres in 700 litres of water	6·43	2·69	4·20	13·32

Additional to these costs is that of transporting water at 15p per 100 litres.

(ii) Knapsack Mistblowers (Output Guide XV/G7)
The recommended dilution rate if 4·5–7 litres in 100–175 litres of water per treated hectare. The costs in Table 17 are based on this range of application rates. Machine cost is taken as 35p per hour.

TABLE 17

APPLICATION OF 2,4,5-T IN WATER TO FOLIAGE
USING A KNAPSACK MISTBLOWER

Rate of Dilution	Labour (£/ha)	Labour Oncost (£/ha)	Herbicide (£/ha)	Machine Charge (£/ha)	Total Cost (£/ha)
4·5 litres in 100 litres of water	2·09	·87	2·70	1·33	6·99
7 litres in 175 litres of water	3·64	1·52	4·20	2·32	11·68

Additional to these costs is the cost of transporting water at 15p per 100 litres.

The table assumes a likely output of 72 litres per hour. If walking conditions are easy and output goes up to 90 litres per hour, the cost per hectare is reduced by about 20%.

(iii) Tractor Mounted Mistblowers (Output Guide XV/G2)
The recommended dilution rates are as for knapsack mistblowers. The machine capital cost is taken as £1705.

TABLE 18

APPLICATION OF 2,4,5-T IN WATER TO FOLIAGE
USING A TRACTOR MOUNTED MISTBLOWER

Application rate/ha	Labour (£/ha)	Labour Oncost (£/ha)	Herbicide (£/ha)	Machine Charge (£/ha)	Total Cost (£/ha)
4·5 litres in 100–175 litres water	0·26	0·10	2·70	0·30	3·36
7 litres in 100–175 litres water	0·26	0·10	4·20	0·30	4·86

Cost of hauling diluent is negligible as the tractor can bring its own bowser to the site.

(iv) Aerial Application
The costs quoted here are based on contractors' quotations and relate to fixed-wing aircraft.

TABLE 19

APPLICATION OF 2,4,5-T IN WATER TO FOLIAGE
USING FIXED WING AIRCRAFT

Application rate/ha	Cost per ha
4·5 litres 2,4,5-T	6·80–7·80
7 litres 2,4,5-T	8·40–9·40

19　Summary of Costs of Foliage Treatment of Woody Weeds

TABLE 20

SUMMARY OF COSTS OF FOLIAGE TREATMENT OF
WOODY WEEDS

Method of Application	Cost per ha including haulage of diluents	
	4·5 litres 2,4,5-T/ha	7 litres 2,4,5-T/ha
Knapsack sprayers	7·8 £/ha	14·4 £/ha
Knapsack mistblowers	7·1　,,	11·9　,,
Tractor mounted mistblowers	3·4　,,	4·9　,,
Aircraft	6·8–7·8 ,,	8·4–9·4 ,,

20　Treatment of Cut Stumps and Basal Bark
The two main herbicides available for this work are Ammonium Sulphamate and 2,4,5-T; usually the unformulated ester of the latter diluted with paraffin is the formulation employed.

Methods available are:

Ammonium Sulphamate applied by watering can or similar device.

2,4,5-T in paraffin applied by knapsack sprayer.

2,4,5-T in paraffin applied by live reel sprayer.

Each is examined in turn:

(i) Ammonium Sulphamate applied by water can or similar device

This work has not been time studied by the Work Study Branch; the following estimate is based on the current recommended dilution rate of 0·4 kg of AMS in 1 litre of water. It is also assumed that the rate of application and the total quantity of liquid required will be about the same as with 2,4,5-T. These assumptions however give AMS the benefit of the doubt; in practice it might well take longer to apply AMS and more liquid per hectare would be required.

TABLE 21

APPLYING AMMONIUM SULPHAMATE IN WATER

Treatment	Labour (£/ha)	Labour Oncost (£/ha)	AMS (£/ha)	Total Cost (£/ha)
140 kg AMS in 350 litres of water/ha	8·23	3·43	26·60	38·26

The cost of transporting water would be of the order of 15p per 100 litres.

(ii) 2,4,5-T in paraffin applied by knapsack sprayer (Output Guide XV/G8)

The following calculations assume a dilution rate of 1·5 litres of 2,4,5-T to 100 litres of paraffin and a total application of 350 litres per hectare.

TABLE 22

APPLYING 2,4,5-T IN PARAFFIN BY KNAPSACK SPRAYER

Treatment	Labour (£/ha)	Labour Oncost (£/ha)	Chemical & Diluent (£/ha)	Total Cost (£/ha)
5·25 litres of 2,4,5-T in 350 litres of paraffin/ha	8·23	3·43	12·93	24·59

The cost per hectare of transporting paraffin would be of the order of 15p per 100 litres.

(iii) 2,4,5-T in paraffin applied by live reel sprayer e.g. Pharos) (Output Guide XV/G8)

Again, a dilution rate of 1·5 litres of 2,4,5-T to 100 litres of paraffin and a total application rate of 350 litres per hectare are assumed.

TABLE 23

APPLYING 2,4,5-T IN PARAFFIN BY LIVE REEL SPRAYER

Treatment	Labour (£/ha)	Labour Oncost (£/ha)	Chemical & Diluent (£/ha)	Machine Charge (£/ha)	Total Cost (£/ha)
5·25 litres of 2,4,5-T in 350 litres of paraffin/ha	7·10	2·96	12·93	2·18	25·17

The cost per hectare of transporting paraffin would be of the order of 15p per 100 litres.

21 Summary of Costs of Treating Cut Stumps and Basal Bark

TABLE 24

SUMMARY OF COSTS OF TREATING CUT STUMPS AND BASAL BARK

Method of Application	Cost per ha including haulage of diluent (£/ha)
Ammonium Sulphamate by water can	38·8
2,4,5-T with knapsack sprayer	25·1
2,4,5-T with live reel sprayer	25·7

22 Tree Injection (Output Guide XV/G9)

Tree injection can be looked upon as an alternative to basal bark application of 2,4,5-T where the standing material is thick enough.

The recommended herbicides are:

50% 2,4,5-T undiluted, or

50% 2,4-D amine undiluted.

The application rate of both chemicals is 1 millilitre at 75 millimetre centres (50 millimetres for resistant species).

If the second example given in para 5 of the output guide (requiring an application rate of 5·6 litres per hectare) is used, costs will be as follows:

TABLE 25

USING TREE INJECTORS TO APPLY 2,4,5-T OR 2,4-D AMINE

Treatment	Labour (£/ha)	Labour Oncost (£/ha)	Chemical (£/ha)	Total Cost (£/ha)
50% 2,4,5-T	5·38	2·24	3·36	10·98
50% 2,4-D Amine	5·38	2·24	2·11	9·73

Costs will of course vary considerably depending upon the difficulty of access, susceptibility of species to the herbicide (and hence number of cuts per stem) and the number of stems per ha. The reader is therefore recommended to use the guide to work out his own costs in the above manner.

23 Cost of Mechanical Weeding

Portable Brushcutter (Standard Time Table XV/1A) As developed at present, these machines are not very effective in dealing with grasses and herbaceous weeds. The cost examples given here therefore relate to woody weeds and climbers in 2·1 m x 2·1 m spacing.

TABLE 26

USING A PORTABLE BRUSHCUTTER

Weed Type	Labour (£/ha)	Labour Oncost (£/ha)	Machine Charge (£/ha)	Total Cost (£/ha)
50% moderate bramble, 50% light coppice	10·37	4·33	5·70	20·40
100% heavy (one year's growth) coppice	18·47	7·71	10·15	36·33

The cost of the brushcutter is taken as 30p per hour. These costs assume 1 year's growth; costs are higher if the vegetation is older.

24 Pedestrian Controlled Machines

These machines are narrow and most suited to 1·5 m x 1·5 m spacing and the job is limited to cutting inter-row vegetation. From studies, a standard time of 623 standard minutes per hectare was recorded using machine A in an area of coarse grasses with some climbers and woody weeds. In 2–3 year old coppice regrowth with brambles, in a spacing of 1·7 x 1·7 m, machine B took 600 standard minutes per hectare. In light woody and herbaceous growth, the same machine took 400 standard minutes.

TABLE 27

USING PEDESTRIAN CONTROLLED WEEDING MACHINES

Machine and Weed Type	Labour (£/ha)	Labour Oncost (£/ha)	Machine Charge (£/ha)	Total Cost (£/ha)
Machine A – Coarse grasses with some climbers and Woody Weeds (1·5 m x 1·5 m spacing)	5·67	2·37	1·43	9·47
Machine B – 2–3 year old coppice regrowth with bramble. (1·7 m x 1·7 m spacing)	5·46	2·28	1·02	8·76
Machine B – Light woody and herbaceous growth. (1·7 m x 1·7 m spacing)	3·64	1·52	0·68	5·84

25 Tractor Powered Rotary Cutting Machines (Rear Mounted) (Output Guide XV/G1)

Output with these machines varies according to row spacing, type of vegetation to be cut and average row length. The time per hectare lays between 366 minutes per ha in light weeds in 1·5 m row spacing to 140 minutes per hectare in dense weeds in 2·1 m spacing. Costs will generally therefore lay within the range shown in Table 28 though can increase with the presence of obstacles, poor tree visibility, etc.

TABLE 28
USING A TRACTOR POWERED
ROTARY CUTTING MACHINE (REAR MOUNTED)

Job Specification	Labour (£/ha)	Labour Oncost (£/ha)	Machine Charge (£/ha)	Total Cost (£/ha)
Weeding with tractor powered rotary weeder: Range of costs	1·30– 3·40	0·53– 1·39	1·38– 3·62	3·21– 8·41
Average cost	2·35	0·96	2·50	5·81

26 Rolling

When rolling heavy grasses and herbs in 2·1 m spacing, time study shows that an output of 3 hectares per day is attainable; in ideal conditions, 4 hectares is possible. Costs will therefore be:

TABLE 29
USING A ROLLER

Job Specification	Labour (£/ha)	Labour Oncost (£/ha)	Machine Charge (£/ha)	Total Cost (£/ha)
Rolling grasses and herbs in 2·1 m row spacing Range of costs	1·12– 1·49	0·46– 0·61	1·26– 1·68	2·84– 3·78
Average cost	1·30	0·53	1·47	3·31

27 Summary of Costs of Weeding by Machine

TABLE 30
SUMMARY OF COSTS OF WEEDING BY MACHINE

Machine	Total Cost (£/ha)
Portable Brushcutter	20·4–36·3
Pedestrian Controlled Machine	5·8–9·5
Tractor Powered rotary machine	3·2–8·4
Rolling	2·8–3·8

These methods are not necessarily alternatives.

Chapter 22

CHOOSING A METHOD

1 Factors

Hand, chemical and mechanical techniques can all be used to weed in most situations whether independently or in combination. A study of Forestry Commission Leaflet 51 and of this Bulletin will help the reader to choose the most suitable method bearing in mind his own circumstances.

2 Questions to be Answered

Before one can decide which is the best way to deal with a weeding situation, a number of questions must be answered. Can a tractor be used? Are there valid reasons why chemicals should not be used? What is the size of the operation? What is the cost likely to be, etc., etc.? The scale of the operation is of relatively minor importance if one assumes that the most expensive item, an agricultural tractor, will generally be available.

3 Difficulties of Comparison

It is difficult to compare different methods of dealing with a weed problem for the end product is often different. Sometimes one application of herbicide will last longer than one machine weeding; sometimes the converse applies. A man with a hook can weed closer to a tree than a tractor mounted weeding machine can, etc. The reader must therefore exercise care in interpreting the tables which follow. Paragraph 2 of the relevant time tables and output guides describes the jobs being done. It must also be emphasised that the figures quoted are limited to the circumstances described in the text of this chapter; if easier or more difficult situations are envisaged, different cost patterns will emerge.

4 Weeding in Grass

TABLE 31
SUMMARY OF COSTS AND METHODS OF WEEDING IN GRASS

Method	Cost per hectare including labour, labour oncost machines and chemicals where applicable
Hand – Light grasses	£6·9–£20·1
Hand – Coarse grasses	£11·0–£25·5
Chemical – Paraquat	£7·7
– Dalapon	£6·7
– Atrazine (spot)	£5·0
(Band)	£8·5
– Chlorthiamid (spot)	£9·2
(Band)	£16·3
Portable Brushcutter	Not recommended
Grass Roller	£2·8–£3·8
Pedestrian Controlled machine	£5·8

5 Woody Weeds and Climbers

TABLE 32
SUMMARY OF COSTS AND METHODS OF WEEDING IN WOODY WEEDS AND CLIMBERS

Method	Cost per hectare including labour, labour oncost, machines, chemicals and diluent where appropriate
Hand – Climbers	£14·6–£30·7
,, – Woody weeds	£17·4–£41·2
Foliage Spraying – Knapsack Sprayers	£7·8–£14·4
– Mistblowers	£7·1–£11·9
– TM Mistblowers	£3·4– £4·9
– Aircraft	£6·8– £9·4
Cut stumps and Basal Bark – AMS	£38·8
– 2,4,5-T Knapsack Sprayers	£25·1
– 2,4,5-T live reel Sprayer	£25·7
Tree injection	£9·7–£11·0
Portable Brushcutter	£20·4–£36·3
Pedestrian Controlled Brushcutter	£5·8– £9·5
Tractor Powered Rotary Cutter	£3·2– £8·4

6 Method Selection

An algorithm, or logical chart, has been prepared (Table 33) which attempts to indicate the best method for the more general types of weeding. It cannot hope to cover *all* possible combinations of circumstances and does not therefore relieve the reader from the need to read the remainder of the book!

7 Conclusion

However, this chart coupled with an intelligent use of the standard time tables and output guides and a thorough knowledge of the site will generally produce the best method.

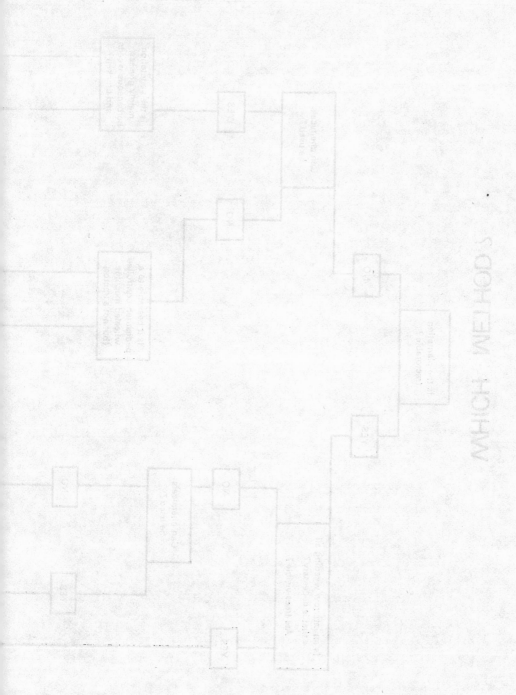

TABLE No 33 FOREST WEEDING ALGORITHM

WHICH METHOD ?

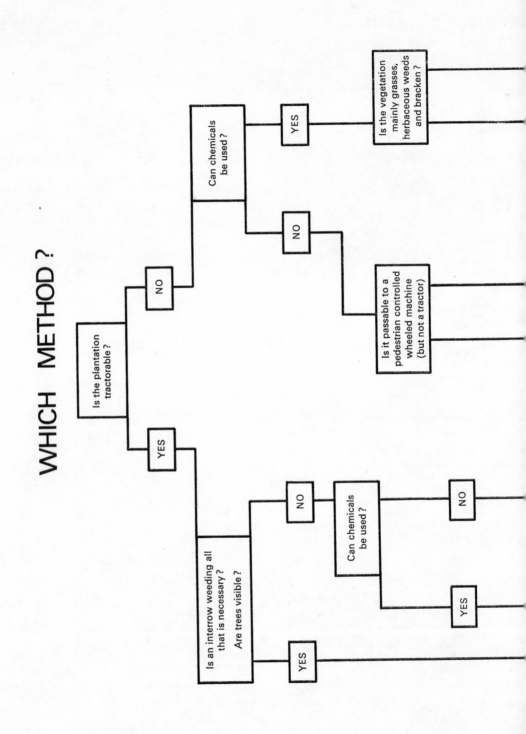

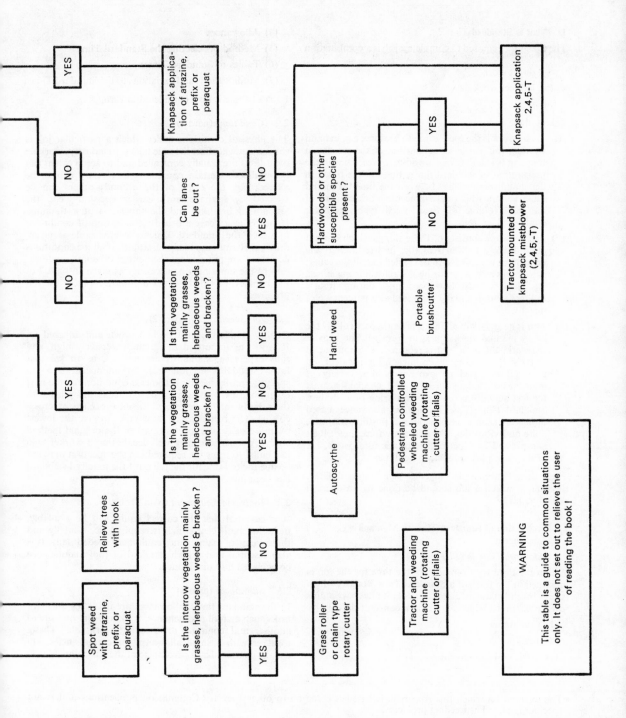

YES — Knapsack application of atrazine, prefix or paraquat

NO — Can lanes be cut?

Can lanes be cut? — NO — Hardwoods or other susceptible species present? — YES — Knapsack application 2,4,5-T

Can lanes be cut? — YES — Hardwoods or other susceptible species present? — NO — Tractor mounted or knapsack mistblower (2,4,5,-T)

NO — Is the vegetation mainly grasses, herbaceous weeds and bracken? — NO — Portable brushcutter

Is the vegetation mainly grasses, herbaceous weeds and bracken? — YES — Hand weed

YES — Is the vegetation mainly grasses, herbaceous weeds and bracken? — NO — Pedestrian controlled wheeled weeding machine (rotating cutter or flails)

Is the vegetation mainly grasses, herbaceous weeds and bracken? — YES — Autoscythe

Relieve trees with hook

Spot weed with atrazine, prefix or paraquat

Is the interrow vegetation mainly grasses, herbaceous weeds & bracken? — NO — Tractor and weeding machine (rotating cutter or flails)

Is the interrow vegetation mainly grasses, herbaceous weeds & bracken? — YES — Grass roller or chain type rotary cutter

WARNING

This table is a guide to common situations only. It does not set out to relieve the user of reading the book!

G

APPENDIX I

STANDARD TIMETABLES AND OUTPUT GUIDES AND THEIR USES ø

1 What is Standard Time ?

The total time required to complete a job is a combination of:

  (i) direct work

  (ii) indirect work

  (iii) rest.

Taking these in turn:

  (i) *Direct work* is the specific job to be done, e.g. in hand weeding this is the actual cutting of the weeds; in thinning it is felling and snedding a tree. During the preparation of standard times, this work is timed in detail and relationships between the time taken and those factors which determine the work content of the job (volume of trees, weed type, etc.) are established.

  (ii) *Indirect work* consists of those things which are not done directly to the trees (or, in weeding, to the weeds) but which have to be carried out all the same; such things as sharpening hooks, refuelling machines, etc. These will also have been timed during studies. Indirect work is usually expressed as a percentage of direct work.

  (iii) *Rest* is necessary in all forms of work, particularly the heavy manual work found in forestry. The heavier the work, the more rest is required. The amount of rest which should be taken in each job is calculated from tables based on experience in a variety of industries including forestry, and checked against the rest actually taken by men during time studies. Standard Time Tables include rest allowances based on factors such as energy output, posture, motions, noise and vibration, dirt and toxic fumes, etc. Rest is expressed as a percentage of the total work, i.e. direct work plus indirect, to be done.

These three factors added together give Standard Time, the time in which a job should be done by an average skilled man.

2 Presentation of Standard Time to Men and Management

2.1 *Standard Time Booklet*

Within the Forestry Commission, the time for the job is presented in the form of a Standard Time Booklet which is very much "standard" in its layout; it always contains seven paragraphs which appear in a constant order:

  (1) Conditions

  (2) Job Specification

  (3) Tools and Equipment

  (4) Allowances

  (5) Method of selecting the Standard Time

  (6) Tables of Standard Times

  (7) Modifications and variations to the Standard Times

Each of these is now considered in turn.

2.2 *Conditions* (para 1)

The physical contitions under which a particular job is carried out will affect the time taken. In industry, working conditions are usually controlled and to some extent can be modified. Certain conditions in forestry cannot be altered, e.g. the slope of the ground; others can be affected by Management's earlier decisions, e.g. the amount of brashing and the timeliness of a thinning. Hence in every case a broad classification of conditions to which the Standard Times are applicable is given, drawing attention to likely variations. If all the conditions described are not present then either (a) some modification to the times may be necessary as given in para 7 of the booklet, or (b) the times may not apply to the job proposed.

2.3 *Job Specification* (para 2)

Quality standards must be laid down and adhered to. It is just as important to see the excessively high, and thus expensive, standards are not set, as to see that lower standards do not creep in unnoticed. The job specification frequently becomes a condition for the next operation, e.g. "poles must be extracted and piled with their butts mainly together" to ensure efficient cross-cutting. The balancing of these tasks to give the lowest overall cost is an important part of the original method study. A supervisor may well decide that a worker who has failed to meet the required job specification may not be due the full rate for the job until the required standard has been met.

2.4 *Tools and Equipment* (para 3)

It is essential that the correct equipment be available, including both gear which is required occasionally and those items of maintenance equipment needed daily. It is also essential that a high standard of tool maintenance be achieved and maintained.

2.5 *Allowances* (para 4)

In the standard times, allowances are made for ancillary tasks such as tool maintenance, walking from one site to another and counting or checking work, etc. These, together with a small allowance for contingencies, are usually expressed as a percentage of the basic time for the

---

øThe material on which this Appendix is based is common to other Forestry Commission publications and is not specifically aimed at weeding problems.

particular job. This "other work" allowance is stated in para 4(a). Rest allowed is shown in 4(b). Para 4(c) is a reminder to management that an incentive allowance must be included in the price per standard minute.

2.6 *Selecting the Standard Time* (para 5)

The purpose of this paragraph is to tell users how to gain entry to the tables in para 6 and what measurements they will need to take beforehand.

2.7 *Tables of Standard Times* (para 6)

These form the central feature of each scheme but are only valid within the conditions, job specification, working methods, and method of evaluation set out in paras 1–4.

2.8 *Modifications and Variations to the Standard Times* (para 7)

Having found the main variables and produced a table of standard times for the whole range, it is generally possible to predict what will happen if certain other subsidiary factors change, e.g. if the plants to be weeded are very small or if there is coppice in a stand to be thinned. Such differences can be allowed for as fixed or percentage alterations to standard times. Naturally the accuracy of these derived times may be less than that for defined jobs but in making a whole series of time studies one or two examples of each change will have been observed. These variations are applied at the Supervisor's discretion using his judgement of the appropriateness of the conditions.

3 Standard Time Tables in Weeding Operations

The following standard time tables appear in Appendix II.

Number	Title
XV/1	Handweeding in Plantations, page 96.
XV/1A	Weeding by Portable Brushcutter in Plantations, page 107.
XV/2	Winter Weeding and Cleaning by Hand, page 118.

4 Uses of Standard Time Tables

Standard Time Tables can be used for the following purposes each of which is considered below:

   (i) As a direct basis for a piecework scheme.

   (ii) As a basis for producing an output guide.

   (iii) To assess performance.

   (iv) To calculate labour requirements.

   (v) To calculate machine requirements.

5 A Piecework Scheme Based on a Standard Time Table

Having first selected the correct standard time for the job (be it a hectare of weeding or the felling of a tree, etc.),

the manager must then convert time to a piecework rate. The generally accepted method within the Forestry Commission is to agree the value of a minute of work with the men's trade union representatives; this is known as the Price per Standard Minute. Then:

Standard Time x Price per Standard Minute = Piecework Rate.

6 Calculating the Price per Standard Minute

By taking the reigning rate of day pay $\dfrac{(£15.68\emptyset}{5} = £3.136)$

and dividing it by the number of minutes in a day (480), the value of one minute of work is arrived at:

$$\frac{£3.136}{480} = £0.0065 \text{ or } 0.65\text{p}.$$

If a worker were paid 0.65p per minute for each minute of work done (and he were an average skilled man), he would earn exactly £15.68 per week but he would not be inclined to give high output because there is no incentive for him to do so.

The Forestry Commission has negotiated with the Trade Unions an agreement which says:

"The piecework rate for any job shall be such that a Skilled Forest Worker is able to earn on piecework in the ordinary weekly hours not less than 30 per cent above his normal time rate for the period he is employed on piecework."

Its staff is therefore given guidance as to how to proceed; the day work price per minute can be increased by 30 per cent to meet the obligations to the Unions. Expressed as a formula, it becomes:

$$\frac{\text{Day pay in pence}}{480} \times \frac{130}{100} = \text{piece rate price per Standard Minute, so:}$$

$$\frac{313.6\text{p}}{480} \times \frac{130}{100} = 0.85\text{p/SM}.$$

The incentive level can of course be varied to compensate for greater responsibility or to encourage greater effort and hence greater output.

7 Output Guides

Output Guides are similar to Standard Time Booklets but para 6 gives either the likely output per hour or per day in terms of quantity of work achievable or the time for the job in minutes. An Output Guide is therefore a guide to managers but leaves them with full responsibility for negotiating the piecework rate. Output Guides are produced:

   (i) Where insufficient data has been collected to produce a full Standard Time Booklet.

   (ii) Where guidance is required by management quickly, i.e. before the full studies are complete.

∅Negotiated rate of pay for a Skilled Forest Worker wef 15 February 1971. This rate was increased to £17.35 on 31.1.72, and to £19.28 on 1.4.73.

(iii) Where data collected in one area (and perhaps published as a Standard Time Booklet) is modified for use in another area.

(iv) Where the expense of producing a full Standard Time Booklet is not justified because of the local nature of the work concerned.

Output Guides are nevertheless as useful to management as are Standard Time Booklets, the only proviso being that they are likely to be less accurate. Standard Time Tables are always statistically validated but sometimes Output Guides are not.

Experience has shown that Standard Time Tables become less accurate as time passes. The Forestry Commission pursues a policy of restudying those tables in extensive use at intervals not exceeding 3 years and thus overcoming this problem. Bearing in mind that this Bulletin was completed in late 1973, the Standard Time Tables printed in it, even though the date on them may be earlier than 1970, can still be used as output guides.

The following output guides are reproduced in Appendix II after the Standard Time Tables:

Number	Title
XV/G1	Weeding with Tractor-powered Weeding Machines, page 126.
XV/G2	Chemical Weeding: Foliar Spraying using the Victair Tractor-mounted Mistblower, page 134.
XV/G3	Chemical Weeding: Application of Atrazine in the Forest, page 137.
XV/G4	Chemical Weeding: Application of Granular Herbicides using a Horstine Farmery Knapsack Applicator, page 143.
XV/G5	Chemical Weeding: Spot Spraying using knapsack sprayers, page 146.
XV/G6	Chemical Weeding: Foliage spraying with 50% 2,4,5-T in water using knapsack sprayers, page 150.
XV/G7	Chemical Weeding: Spraying herbicides with knapsack mistblowers, page 153.
XV/G8	Chemical Weeding, Cleaning and preparing ground: Cut stump and Basal Bark Treatment with 100% 2,4,5-T in Paraffin using (A) knapsack Sprayers, or (B) Pharos, page 157.
XV/G9	Chemical Weeding: Tree injection using a Swedish water pistol and a Boy Scout axe, page 164.

8 Calculating Output and Performance from Standard Time Tables

If the standard time for a job – say felling and snedding a tree – is 10 standard minutes (usually expressed as 10 SMs) then the output for an 8-hour day at standard performance is:

$$\frac{\text{Minutes at work daily}}{\text{Standard Minutes for job}} = \frac{8 \text{ hrs. x } 60 \text{ mins.}}{10 \text{ SMs}} = 48 \text{ trees per day}$$

It should be noted that a man will not in fact take 10 minutes to fell and sned a tree at standard performance but perhaps 7 or 8; the balance being other work and rest

that occurs at other times of the day. The output as calculated above is for one man; if as part of the specified conditions of the job two or more men are obliged to work together, as on some machines, e.g. sawbench or peeler, then the output for that machine is:

$$\frac{\text{Minutes at work daily}}{\text{Standard Minutes for job}} \text{ x No. of operators}$$

The actual output of a less skilled or day-worker and a highly skilled piece worker will vary considerably and might range from say 36 to 60 units per day. Standard performance (i.e. that achieved by a skilled worker under incentive conditions) is expressed as 100. The output given above can be expressed relative to this and the performance calculated:

Output	Output at 100	Performance
36	48	$\frac{36}{48}$ x 100 = 75
60	48	$\frac{60}{48}$ x 100 = 125

Combining these two calculations into general terms, *performance* can be defined:

$$\frac{\text{Output expressed in standard time}}{\text{Time on job}} \text{ x } 100$$

e.g. with an output of 60 units of 10 Standard Minutes in an 8-hour day it is:

$$\frac{60 \text{ units x } 10 \text{ SMs x } 100}{8 \text{ hours x } 60 \text{ mins}} = \text{a performance of } 125.$$

In forestry more than in manufacturing industries, performance over short periods may appear to vary widely when in fact it is local variation in conditions that is responsible. However, performances over periods of more than a few days which consistently fall outside the limits of 70–130 need investigation, because the job or conditions may have changed or the standard data been incorrectly applied. It should be noted that a performance of 75 represents, approximately, day work output whilst a performance of 130 is not seen very often during studies and is regarded as exceptional. Management is, of course, free to investigate lesser variations.

Similar calculations, though somewhat less precise, can be made using output guides.

9 Calculating Labour Requirements using Standard Time Tables

Example: To fell and sned a stand of 4000 Douglas fir average volume 0·55 m³ in a week (5 days). How many men does the manager need?

Using Standard Time Table XVIII/19, the time for 1 tree is 12·66 standard minutes.

∴ the time for the stand is 12·66 x 4000 = 50,640 minutes.

As there are 2400 minutes per man per week available,

the number of men required is: $\frac{50,640}{2400} = 21$ men.

For reasons of safety, it might be as well to use six men and take a month to do the job!

Similar calculations, though somewhat less precise, can be made using output guides.

10 Machine Requirements

The calculation is similar to that for labour.

Example: The job is to peel 11,500 m³ of poles averaging 0·09 m³ each and 8 metres long per annum using a Cambio 35 peeler. Can the machine cope with this throughput in a year of 200 days without resorting to overtime or shift working?

Table XX/7 gives a standard time of 18·57 minutes per 100 metres peeled, but this is the time for 2 men hence it must be divided by 2 to find the time the machine will take:

$$\text{Machine time per 100 m} = \frac{18.57}{2} = 9.29 \text{ minutes.}$$

Total length of poles to be peeled =

$$\frac{11500}{0.09} \text{ x 8 metres} = 1,022,222 \text{ metres}$$

$$\therefore \text{ total no of days required} = \frac{1,022,222}{480 \times 100} \text{ x } 9.29 = 198$$

days, or one year almost exactly!

Hence the machine can cope.

In practice, however, ½ day per week (4 hours) must be allowed for machine maintenance, hence 4 hours overtime working a week must be introduced so that the required quantity can be peeled in the time allowed.

Similar calculations, though somewhat less precise, can be made using output guides.

APPENDIX   II

STANDARD TIME TABLES

AND

OUTPUT GUIDES:

EXAMPLES

WARNING

These Tables have been produced by the
Forestry Commission specially for their
conditions. The Commission cannot
therefore be held responsible for any
losses arising from their use (or misuse)
in circumstances outside the Commission's
jurisdiction

Section	XV
No.	1
Date	Sept. 1969 (Reissued 1973)

STANDARD TIMES FOR HANDWEEDING IN PLANTATIONS

1.   CONDITIONS

The Standard Times apply to weeding in these conditions:

a.   Obstructions to walking ie stumps, lop and top, drains etc. as normally present on a forest floor, but see paragraph 7a.

b.   Slopes up to 25% but see paragraph 7b.

c.   Few trees visible above the surrounding vegetation but fairly easily found by parting the vegetation with the hook; but see paragraph 7c.

2.   JOB SPECIFICATION

The Standard Times are for the following work but see paragraph 7d.

a.   Cut a swath 1 metre wide leaving the stubble 15-25 cm between plants and 8-15cm high around plants. Interrow vegetation is to be topped only if it is high enough or likely to become high enough to fall on the trees.

b.   Cut vegetation is to be kept clear of major drains, footpaths and rides.

3.   TOOLS AND EQUIPMENT

a.   Where vegetation is predominantly B2, or B3: Reap hook, Bean hook, or Dutch weeding scythe.

b.   One year's growth of other vegetation: Light brushing hook S-hook or Bean hook.

c.   More than one year's growth of woody weeds and climbers: Heavy brushing hook or S-hook.

Plate 32. The Mk III grass roller fitted with retracting road wheels. The photograph shows the wheels in position for travelling on metalled roads. The power unit is a narrow gauge Massey Ferguson MF 135 Vineyard tractor. WS 4/85

Plate 33. The Mk III roller with road wheels retracted for rolling. It is shown here attached to a Holder AG 35F Frame-steered tractor. WS 3/13/16

Plate 34. A 600-gallon (2728 litres) paraffin storage tank at Wymersley Forest (Northants). It is mounted sufficiently high to fill the transporting vehicle by gravity. WS 4/1/3

Plate 35. A continuously pumped knapsack sprayer, the Cooper, Pegler CP 3, with a 'Politec' tree guard spraying paraquat around a tree. WS 2/37/31

Plate 36. The CP3 with 'Politec'. The trigger control is in the worker's right hand and the pump handle in his left. He is protected by an Abridge polyurethane suit. WS 2/37/32

Plate 37. The 'Politec' tree guard for use with a CP3 knapsack sprayer when spraying paraquat or dalapon.

Plate 38. Spray shields for use with the CP 3 knapsack sprayer. WS 2/48/18

Plate 39. A spray shield made from a plastic washing up bowl and a 'Politec' lance and handle.
WS 4/83

Plate 40. The underside of a tree spraying attachment made from a plastic Gramoxone container and a standard 21″ (53 cm) lance. WS 2/49/23

Plates 41 and 42. The Geeco No. 148 dribble bar. Inset (plate 42) shows a close up of the spraying head. WS 2/95/4 and WS 2/95/6

Plate 43. The Jim Gem tree injector. WS 2/38/37

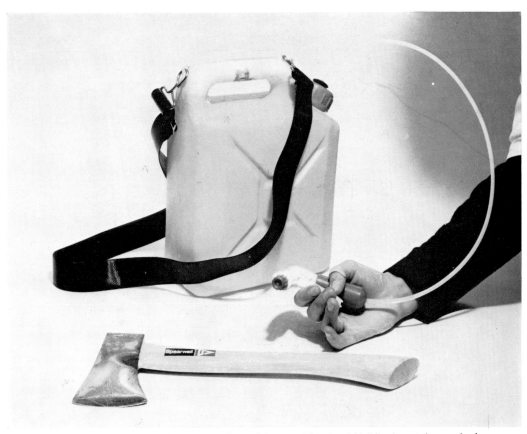

Plate 44. The Swedish "Fickningsspruta" tree injector with a 1-gal (4·5 litre) container and a boy scout hatchet. B6606

Plate 45. The Stihl SG 17 knapsack mistblower. WS 2/35/16

Plate 46. The Horstine Farmery knapsack granule applicator. WS 2/35/14

4. <u>ALLOWANCES</u>
<u>Included in the Standard Time</u>

   a. For contingencies and work other than the actual weeding, eg. sharpening hook, walking in and out, general preparation; pack up, walking between work sites, unavoidable delay etc. : 10% of the time spent weeding.

   b. Personal needs and rest: 20% of the total working time.

   <u>To be included in the Price per Standard Minute</u>

   c. The appropriate incentive allowance.

5. <u>METHOD OF SELECTING THE STANDARD TIME</u>

   a. Define:

      1) The major weed groups present:

      A. Bracken, herbaceous plants and soft grasses

      B. Coarse grasses and rush

      C. Climbers, mostly Bramble

      D. Woody weeds (Coppice and seedlings)

      2) The grade of difficulty of each group (see appendix)

      3) The cover of each group as a percentage of the area to be cut, estimated in steps of 5%.

NB. The area may include a percentage of ground where weed growth is not competing with the crop and does not therefore require cutting. A time must however be allocated to these areas where it is impracticable to avoid walking them when cutting (see paragraph 6).

   b. <u>CONVERT THE INDICES OF COVER AND DIFFICULTY INTO STANDARD TIME</u>

      (i) Table 6 give the Standard Times for cutting the four major weed groups. The Times are shown according to the grade of difficulty and the spacing. Using the gradings obtained from the Appendix look up the Standard Times for weeding one hectare of each major weed group.

(ii)   Multiply the times by the cover percentages.

(iii) Add together the times allocated to each of the
       major weed groups to find the Standard Time for
       weeding one hectare.

(iv)   Example of weed assessment and calculation of
       Standard Time:

Weed Assessment Table

Major Weed Group	Grade	% Cover	Standard Time per hectare *	% Cover	Standard Time per hectare
Herbaceous Plants	2	50	1000	50%	500
Coarse Grasses	1	10	900	10%	90
Climbers	2	15	1950	15%	293
Woody Weeds	3	25	3350	25%	837
Total		100%			1720

* From Table 6, 2.1m spacing

NOTE: Set rate for areas which will be weeded in one to six weeks,
       ie for relatively large blocks — whole compartments, rather
       than small parts of compartments.

6. WEEDING BY HAND TOOLS-TIME PER HECTARE IN STANDARD MINUTES

WEED GROUP	GRADE	PLANT SPACINGS (metres)							
		2.1x2.1	2.0x2.0	1.9x1.9	1.8x1.8	1.7x1.7	1.6x1x6	1.5x1x5	1.4x1.4
A. HERBS,BRACKEN AND MOST SOFT GRASSES e.g. Foxglove, Willow herb, Meadow sweet, Sorrel and Thistle and other wild flowers GRASSES: e.g. Agrostis, Holcus, Cocksfoot, non-tussocky Molinia etc	1	560	590	630	670	710	750	800	850
	2	1000	1040	1090	1150	1210	1290	1380	1490
	3	1630	1710	1800	1900	2020	2150	2290	2440
B. COARSE GRASSES AND RUSH e.g. Deschampsia caespitosa, Calamagrostis, tussocky Molinia etc.	1	900	950	1010	1070	1130	1200	1270	1340
	2	1330	1390	1470	1560	1660	1770	1900	2040
	3	2070	2160	2270	2400	2550	2710	2890	3090
C. CLIMBERS Principally Bramble, Briar, also Honeysuckle, Clematis	1	1190	1240	1300	1380	1460	1560	1660	1780
	2	1950	2050	2160	2290	2430	2590	2760	2950
	3	2490	2530	2580	2650	2740	2850	2970	3100
D. WOODY WEEDS Coppice and Seedlings, Gorse and Broom included	1	1410	1470	1540	1630	1730	1830	1950	2090
	2	2490	2530	2580	2650	2740	2850	2970	3110
	3	3350	3390	3480	3620	3800	4030	4320	4650
AREAS NOT REQUIRING ANY CUTTING (See 5a - 3)		150	155	160	170	180	190	200	210

NOTE: INTERPOLATE BETWEEN GRADES WHERE NECESSARY

7.   MODIFICATIONS AND VARIATIONS TO THE STANDARD TIMES

Note: These modifications should be applied at the forester's discretion using his judgement as to the appropriateness of the conditions.

a. Below average ground conditions

Where the obstructions to walking are more than normally present on a forest floor eg. lop and top from previous crop not burnt, fallen boughs from ringed trees, mineworkings, unstable slopes

ADD up to 20% in steps of 5%

b. Steep Slopes

The Standard Times are for slopes up to 25%. On steeper slopes add to the standard times as follows:

Range of Slope	% increase in time
Over 25% – 35%	5%
Over 35% – 45%	10%
Over 45%	15%

c. Visibility of Trees

Modify the Standard times as follows:

Degree of difficulty in finding trees	Description	Modification
Easy	Most leaders visible above vegetation; remainder of trees can be seen readily when vegetation is parted.	Subtract 10%
Moderate	Few trees visible above surrounding vegetation but fairly easily found by parting the vegetation with the hook.	Standard
Difficult	Trees well below the level of the vegetation; much searching required with stick or hook. Usually associated with small or poorly furnished trees.	Add 10%
Very Difficult	Trees well below the level of the vegetation; much searching required with the point of the hook. May have to cut over vegetation to next larger tree then retrace steps to find intermediate tree. Usually associated with very small trees in thick grass.	Add 20%

Note: When many trees are missing, tend to downgrade visibility

d. Variation to Job Specification

When the job specification requires more or less to be cut than the specification given in paragraph 2a. Add or subtract in steps of 5% up to 15%.

e. Ploughed Ground

(i) On sites where weed growth is suppressed in the furrows and weeding is done by working along the ridge, Standard Times may be reduced by 5% steps up to 20%.

(ii) On sites where weed growth is vigorous and widespread and where unstable ridges make it necessary to work from the furrows, Standard Times may be increased by 5% or 10%.

f. Two-Three Seasons' Growth

The Standard Times are for one season's growth. On sites where weeding has not been done for one or two years, the Coarse Grasses and Rush will have formed a tuft of dead vegetation, the Standard Time may be increased by 10% per year's dead growth; for Woody Weeds and Climbers the Standard Times may be increased by 25% per year to allow for the larger tougher growth.

g. Exceptionally Heavy Grass and Herbaceous Growth

On sites where the full summer's weed growth is exceptionally heavy, eg. dense Bracken 7' (2.1 metres) high where it is necessary to pile the Bracken deliberately between the rows, Standard Times for Grade 3 may be increased by 5% steps up to 20%.

h. Underplanted Larch Plantations

Where there is a rank growth of Deschampsia flexuosa, Anthoxanthum, Festuca etc. Standard Times for tough Grasses may be increased in steps of 5% up to 20%.

i. Overhead Cover

There is no indication that the work content of weeding under overhead cover is different from weeding comparable grades of vegetation in the open.

j. Prolonged Spells of Very Hot weather. Add 5%

APPENDIX TO TABLE XV/1

GUIDE FOR ASSESSING THE DIFFICULTY OF CUTTING WEED GROWTH

Three grades of difficulty are recognised in each of the four major weed groups.

The assessment comprises two factors; the density of the weed stems and the growth characteristics i.e. height, thickness and toughness. The grade of difficulty is the combination of these two factors. If necessary Foresters should interpolate between grades.

Example of weed assessment:-

1. An area to be weeded for the second year has a growth of bramble. The bramble plants are about 1.8m apart and the runners are thin and trailing along the ground. The area should clearly be assigned to Grade I, light climbers.

2. The same area is to be weeded for the fourth year. The bramble plants are growing closely, only about 0.6m apart; the previous weeding was done late in the summer and the runners are numerous but thin and short. The bramble shows some characteristics of heavy growth and some of light growth. The correct assessment would be moderate.

The characteristics described in the following tables are intended as a guide only and reasonable tolerance should be allowed in the measurements given, in particular height, which can vary considerably without seriously altering the difficulty. Generally it is the density and thickness of stems which determines the cutting times.

NOTE   Stem density should only be assessed in pure patches of the vegetation in question.

A. BRACKEN and Other Ferns

Grade	Height	Thickness	Density of stems	General description of factors indicating grade
1. Light	0.6-0.8 m	5mm	Possible to walk without crushing Bracken stems	Bracken canopy not dense enough to conceal bare ground or grass growing around the fronds. Typical of Bracken sites in Spring. On sites where Bracken growth is light or moderate throughout the season other weeds found are typically soft grasses and herbaceous plants.
2. Moderate	0.6-1.2 m	Mostly 5-12 mm	About a boot width apart	Bracken canopy mostly conceals bare ground, short grass and small trees. Typical of Bracken sites in early summer.
3. Heavy	1.0-1.5 m	5-12 mm	Mostly 5-8 cm	Bracken canopy completely conceals bare ground and small trees. Typical growth of late summer and of sites where Bracken grows well and has suppressed most other weeds. Cut fronds tend to fall back on the worker and require keeping in the rows with more deliberation than in 1 and 2

A. HERBACEOUS PLANTS. Willow Herb, Foxglove, Meadow Sweet, Spurge
　　　　　　　　　　　and other Wild Flowers; Thistle, Butterbur;
　　　　　　　　　　　Soft grasses, eg. Agrostis, Holcus, Cocksfoot.

GRADE	HEIGHT	THICKNESS	DENSITY OF STEMS	GENERAL DESCRIPTION OF FACTORS INDICATING GRADES
1. Light	0.6 m		Scattered stems	Growth not dense enough to conceal ground and small trees. Typical Spring growth on moist sites. Generally a site growing mostly herbs classified as light would not require weeding. Grade I is usually given where herbs occur in mixture with tougher weeds such as coppice and bramble.
2. Moderate	0.6-1.1m		Up to 0.1 per sq m.	Weed growth mostly dense enough to conceal ground and small trees. Flowering plants in flower. Typical summer growth on moist sites.
3. Heavy	0.9 m		More than 0.1 per sq m.	Ground and small trees concealed. Flowering plants in flower or seed. Dense lower storey of soft grasses which requires cutting.

B. COARSE GRASSES AND RUSH　eg Deschampsia caespitosa

1. Light	1 m		Scattered Stems	Thin covering of grass stalks. Would probably not require cutting if it were the only weed.
2. Moderate	Up to 1 m		Small Clumps	Fairly dense covering Deschampsia forming occasional awkward clumps.
3. Heavy	1m and over		Large and frequent clumps	Dense covering. Tough and difficult to cut whether wet or dry.

Note: Soft grasses can become tough or wiry in the autumn and thought
　　　of as coarse grass

C. CLIMBERS. Bramble, Rosebriar, Raspberry Cane, Honeysuckle.
1 year's growth

Grade	Height	Thickness	Density of stems	General Description of factors indicating grade
BRAMBLE 1.	up to 0.6m	Up to 5mm	Plants mostly more than 1.2m apart	Typical bramble colonisation in first year or two after planting eg. Trailing along ground, occasional runners arching and beginning to interlace. Not bushy and with few or dead stems from previous year's growth.
2.	0.3-0.6m with longer runners	Mostly 5-10mm	Plants mostly 1-1.2m apart	Mostly bushy. Runners from different plants frequently interlacing. Climbs high into trees or coppice when opportunities occur.
3.	Mostly over 0.6m with long runners	up to 12.mm	Plants mostly 0.6-0.9m apart	Dense bushes, difficult to walk through. Many tough, dead stems from previous year's growth. Requires repeated strokes with the hook making rhythmic cutting difficult. Long handled hook required.

Note: Honeysuckle and Rosebriar are not commonly found colonising large areas and are not described here.

Raspberry canes form dense patches. They are softer than bramble, do not bush so densely and rarely justify a grading of 3.

H

D. <u>COPPICE REGROWTH AND SEEDLINGS</u>. ONE YEARS GROWTH. THICKNESS
CLASSIFICATION DEPENDS ON THE HEIGHT AT WHICH GROWTH IS TO BE CUT

GRADE	HEIGHT	THICKNESS	DENSITY OF STEMS	GENERAL DESCRIPTION OF FACTORS INDICATING GRADE
1. Light	Varies considerably up to 1 metre	Mostly up to 5 mm	Stumps up to 4m or more apart along the rows. Up to a score of shoots per stump, seedlings scattered.	Early season's growth. Soft, green and fairly easy to cut with reap hook. Alternatively, late season's growth, but with Coppice stems very thin.
2. Moderate	Up to 1.2 metres	Mostly 5-20 mm	Stumps 2.5-4m apart along the rows 20-30 shoots per stump.	Usually late season's growth. Tough, often requires repeated blows when using a reap hook.
3. Heavy	1.2 metres and above	Mostly more than 10 mm	Stumps frequent. More than 30 shoots on many stumps.	Late season's growth. Coppice requires repeated blows. Long handled reap hook or light brushing hook preferred.

<u>NOTE:</u>

<u>WOODY WEEDS variations in toughness</u>

Some species are much tougher and more difficult to cut than others,
eg. Oak, Alder, Ash, Hazel, Broom and Gorse and where these comprise
the bulk of woody weed growth they may require a higher grading than
the more common mixture where softer species such as Willow, Sycamore,
Birch and Elder are included.

Section	XV
No	1A
Date	1966 (reissued 1973)

STANDARD TIMES FOR WEEDING BY PORTABLE BRUSHCUTTER IN PLANTATIONS

1. ### CONDITIONS

   The Standard Times apply to weeding under the following conditions:

   a. Obstructions to walking, ie stumps, lop and top, drains etc as normally present on a forest floor but see paragraph 7a.

   b. Slopes up to 25% but see paragraph 7b.

2. ### JOB SPECIFICATION

   The Standard Times are for the following work but see paragraph 7d.

   a. Cut a swath 1 metre wide leaving the stubble 15–25cm between plants and 8–15cm high around plants. Inter-row vegetation is to be topped only if it is high enough or likely to become high enough to fall on the trees.

   b. Cut weeds to be kept clear of major drains, footpaths and rides.

3. ### TOOLS AND EQUIPMENT

   a. Husqvarna or other similar portable brushcutter with two spare blades.

   b. A one gallon (5 litre) can for fuel

   c. Spare sparking plug

   d. Feeler gauge

   e. Maintenance schedule

   f. Filler funnel with filter

   g. Box in which to store machine

   h. Protective gloves and apron

4.   ALLOWANCES

Included in the Standard Time

a. For contingencies and work other than the actual weeding,
    e.g. maintenance and breakdowns of less than 30 minutes,
    walking between work sites, etc.: 21% of the time spent
    weeding.

b. Personal needs and rest: 15% of the total working time.

To be included in the price per Standard Minute

c. The appropriate incentive allowance.

5.   METHOD OF SELECTING THE STANDARD TIME

a. Define:

1) The major weed groups present:

A. Bracken, herbaceous plants and soft grasses

B. Coarse grasses and rush

C. Climbers, mostly Bramble

D. Woody weeds (Coppice and seedlings)

2) The grade of difficulty of each group (see appendix)

3) The cover of each group as a percentage of the area to be
    cut, estimated in steps of 5%.

N.B. The area may include a percentage of ground where weed
growth is not competing with the crop and does not therefore
require cutting. A time must however be allocated to these
areas where it is impracticable to avoid walking them when
cutting (see paragraph 6).

b. CONVERT THE INDICES OF COVER AND DIFFICULTY INTO STANDARD
    TIME

    (i)   Table 6 gives the Standard Times for cutting the
          four major weed groups. The Times are shown
          according to the grade of difficulty and the
          spacing. Using the gradings obtained from the
          Appendix look up the Standard Times for weeding one
          hectare of each major weed group.

    (ii) Multiply the times by the cover percentages.

(iii) Add together the times allocated to each of the major weed groups to find the Standard Time for weeding one hectare.

(iv) Example of weed assessment and calculation of Standard Time:

Weed Assessment

Major Weed Group	Grade	% Cover	Standard Time per hectare Ø	% Cover	Standard Time per hectare
Herbaceous Plants	2	50	1250	50	625
Coarse Grasses	1	10	1180	10	118
Climbers	2	15	1810	15	271
Woody Weeds	3	25	2960	25	740
TOTAL		100			1754

Ø From Table 6, 1.5 m spacing.

NOTE: Set rate for areas which will be weeded in one to six weeks, i.e. for relatively large blocks — whole compartments, rather than small parts of compartments.

6. WEEDING BY PORTABLE BRUSHCUTTER - TIME PER HECTARE IN STANDARD MINUTES

WEED GROUP	GRADE	PLANT SPACING (metres)							
		2.1x2.1	2.0x2.0	1.9x1.9	1.8x1.8	1.7x1.7	1.6x1.6	1.5x1.5	1.4x1.4
A. HERBS,BRACKEN AND MOST SOFT GRASSES									
e.g. Foxglove, Willow herb, Meadow Sweet, Sorrel and Thistle and other	1	720	770	820	870	920	970	1030	1080
wild flowers GRASSES; e.g. Agrostis, Holcus, Cocksfoot, non - tussocky Molinia	2	840	910	980	1050	1120	1190	1250	1320
etc;	3	1040	1120	1200	1280	1350	1430	1500	1570
B. COARSE GRASSES AND RUSH									
e.g. Deschampsia caespitosa,	1	620	720	820	910	1000	1100	1180	1270
Calamagrostis,	2	1010	1100	1180	1260	1340	1420	1490	1550
tussocky Molinia etc	3	1210	1310	1400	1500	1600	1690	1780	1870
C. CLIMBERS Principally	1	960	1030	1100	1170	1250	1310	1380	1450
Bramble, Briar, also Honeysuckle,	2	1240	1330	1420	1510	1610	1710	1810	1910
Clematis	3	1530	1650	1770	1890	2020	2140	2260	2380
D. WOODY WEEDS Coppice and	1	1040	1120	1200	1280	1350	1430	1500	1570
Seedlings, Gorse and Broom included	2	1530	1650	1770	1890	2020	2140	2260	2380
	3	2030	2180	2340	2490	2650	2800	2960	3120
AREAS NOT REQUIRING ANY CUTTING (See 5a - 3)		150	155	160	170	180	190	200	210

NOTE: INTERPOLATE BETWEEN GRADES WHERE NECESSARY

7. MODIFICATIONS AND VARIATIONS TO THE STANDARD TIMES

Note: These modifications should be applied at the Forester's discretion using his judgement as to the appropriateness of the conditions

a. Below average ground conditions

Where the obstructions to walking are more than normally present on a forest floor, e.g. lop and top from previous crop not burnt, fallen boughs from ringed trees, mineworkings, unstable slopes

ADD up to 20% in
steps of 5%

b. Steep slopes

The Standard Times are for slopes up to 25%. On steeper slopes add to the standard times as follows:-

Range of Slope	% increase in time
Over 25% – 35%	5%
Over 35% – 45%	10%
Over 45%	15%

c. Visibility of Trees

Modify the Standard Times as follows:-

Degree of difficulty in finding trees	Description	Modification
Easy	Most leaders visible above vegetation; remainder of trees can be seen readily when vegetation is parted.	Subtract 10%
Moderate	Few trees visible above surrounding vegetation but fairly easily found.	Standard
Difficult	Trees well below the level of the vegetation; much searching required. Usually associated with small or poorly furnished trees.	Add 10%
Very Difficult	Trees well below the level of the vegetation; much searching required. May have to cut over vegetation to next larger tree then retrace steps to find intermediate tree. (Usually associated with very small trees in thick grass).	Add 20%

Note: When many trees are missing, tend to downgrade visibility

d.   Variation to Job Specification

When the job specification requires more or less to be cut
than the specification given in paragraph 2a.   Add or subtract
in steps of 5% up to 15%.

e.   Ploughed Ground

   (i)   On sites where weed growth is suppressed in the furrows
         and weeding is done by working along the ridges,
         Standard Times may be reduced by 5% steps up to 20%.

   (ii) On sites where weed growth is vigorous and widespread
         and where unstable ridges make it necessary to work
         from the furrows, Standard Times may be increased by 5%
         or 10%.

f.   Two-Three Seasons' Growth

The Standard Times are for one season's growth.   On sites where
weeding has not been done for one or two years, the Standard
Times for Woody Weeds and Climbers may be increased by 25% per
year to allow for the larger tougher growth.

g.   Overhead Cover

There is no indication that the work content of weeding under
overhead cover is different from weeding comparable grades of
vegetation in the open.

h.   Prolonged Spells of Very Hot Weather

During prolonged spells of very hot weather add 5%.

APPENDIX TO TABLE XV/1A

GUIDE FOR ASSESSING THE DIFFICULTY OF CUTTING WEED GROWTH

Three grades of difficulty are recognised in each of the four major weed groups.

The assessment comprises two factors; the density of the weed stems and the growth characteristics i.e. height, thickness and toughness. The grade of difficulty is the combination of these two factors. If necessary Foresters should interpolate between grades.

Example of weed assessment:-

1) An area to be weeded for the second year has a growth of bramble. The bramble plants are about 1.8m apart and the runners are thin and trailing along the ground. The area should clearly be assigned to Grade I, light climbers.

2) The same area is to be weeded for the fourth year. The bramble plants are growing closely, only about 0.6m apart; the previous weeding was done late in the summer and the runners are numerous but thin and short. The bramble shows some characteristics of heavy growth and some of light growth. The correct assessment would be moderate.

The characteristics described in the following tables are intended as a guide only and reasonable tolerance should be allowed in the measurements given, in particular height, which can vary considerably without seriously altering the difficulty. Generally it is the density and thickness of stems which determine the cutting times.

NOTE Stem density should only be assessed in pure patches of the vegetation in question.

A. BRACKEN and Other Ferns

Grade	Height	Thickness	Density of Stems	General description of factors indicating grade
1. Light	0.6 - 0.8 m	5mm	Possible to walk without crushing Bracken Stems	Bracken canopy not dense enough to conceal bare ground or grass growing around the fronds. Typical of Bracken sites in Spring. On sites where Bracken growth is light or moderate throughout the season other weeds found are typically soft grasses and herbaceous plants.
2. Moderate	0.6 - 1.2 m	Mostly 5-12mm	About a boot width apart	Bracken canopy mostly conceals bare ground, short grass and small trees. Typical of Bracken sites in early summer.
3. Heavy	1.0 - 1.5 m	5 - 12mm	Mostly 5 - 8 cm apart	Bracken canopy completely conceals bare ground and small trees. Typical growth of late summer and of sites where Bracken grows well and has suppressed most other weeds. Cut fronds tend to fall back on the worker and require keeping in the rows with more deliberation than in 1 and 2.

A. <u>HERBACEOUS PLANTS</u>. Willow Herb, Foxglove, Meadow Sweet, Spurge and other Wild Flowers; Thistle, Butterbur; Soft grasses, eg. <u>Agrostis</u>, <u>Holcus</u>, Cocksfoot.

Grade	Height	Thickness	Density of stems	General description of factors indicating grade
1. Light	0.6 m		Scattered stems	Growth not dense enough to conceal ground and small trees. Typical Spring growth on moist sites. Generally a site growing mostly herbs classified as light would not require weeding. Grade I is usually given where herbs occur in mixture with tougher weeds such as coppice bramble.
2. Moderate	0.6–1.1m		Up to 0.1 per sq m.	Weed growth mostly dense enough to conceal ground and small trees. Flowering plants in flower. Typical summer growth on moist sites.
3. Heavy	0.9 m		More than 0.1 per sq m	Ground and small trees concealed. Flowering plants in flower or seed. Dense lower storey of soft grasses which requires cutting.
B. COARSE GRASSES AND RUSH eg <u>Deschampsia caespitosa</u>				
1. Light	1m		Scattered stems	Thin covering of grass stalks. Would probably not require cutting if it were the only weed.
2. Moderate	Up to 1 m		Small clumps	Fairly dense covering, Deschampsia forming occasional awkward clumps.
3. Heavy	1m and over		Large and frequent clumps	Dense covering. Tough and difficult to cut whether wet or dry.

Note: Soft grasses can become tough or wiry in the autumn and thought of as coarse grass.

C. CLIMBERS. Bramble, Rosebriar, Raspberry Cane, Honeysuckle.
        1 year's growth

Grade	Height	Thickness	Density of stems	General Description of factors indicating grade
BRAMBLE				
1.	Up to 0.6m	Up to 5mm	Plants mostly more than 1.2m apart	Typical bramble colonisation in first year or two after planting eg. Trailing along ground occasional runners arching and beginning to interlace. Not bushy and with few or dead stems from previous year's growth.
2.	0.3-0.6m with longer runners	Mostly 5-10mm	Plants mostly 1-1.2 m apart	Mostly bushy. Runners from different plants frequently interlacing. Climbs high into trees or coppice when opportunities occur.
3.	Mostly over 0.6m with long	Up to 12 m	Plants mostly 0.6-0.9m apart	Dense bushes, difficult to walk through Many tough dead stems from previous year's growth. Requires repeated strokes with the hook making ryhthmic cutting difficult. Long handled hook required.

Note: Honeysuckle and Rosebriar are not commonly found colonising large areas and are not described here.

Raspberry canes form dense patches. They are softer than bramble, do not bush so densely and rarely justify a grading of 3.

D. <u>COPPICE REGROWTH AND SEEDLINGS</u>. ONE YEARS GROWTH. THICKNESS
   CLASSIFICATION DEPENDS ON THE HEIGHT AT WHICH GROWTH IS TO BE CUT

GRADE	HEIGHT	THICKNESS	DENSITY OF STEMS	GENERAL DESCRIPTION OF FACTORS INDICATING GRADE
1. Light	Varies considerably up to 1 metre	Mostly up to 5mm	Stumps up to 4m or more apart along the rows. Up to a score of shoots per stump, seedlings scattered.	Early season's growth. Soft, green and fairly easy to cut with reap hook. Alternatively late seasons growth, but Coppice stems very thin.
2. Moderate	Up to 1.2 metres	Mostly 5 – 20mm	Stumps 2.5 – 4m apart along the rows 20–30 shoots per stump.	Usually late season's growth. Tough, often requires repeated blows when using a reap hook.
3. Heavy	1.2 metres and above	Mostly more than 10mm	Stumps frequent. More than 30 shoots on many stumps.	Late season's growth. Coppice requires repeated blows. Long handled reap hook or light brushing hook preferred.

<u>NOTE:</u>

<u>WOODY WEEDS variations in toughness</u>

Some species are much tougher and more difficult to cut than others,
eg Oak, Alder, Ash, Hazel, Broom and Gorse and where these comprise
the bulk of woody weed growth they may require a higher grading than
the more common mixture where softer species such as Willow,
Sycamore, Birch and Elder are included.

Section	XV
No	2
Date	1971 (Reissued 1973)

STANDARD TIMES FOR

WINTER WEEDING AND CLEANING IN PLANTATIONS

BY HAND

1. CONDITIONS

The Standard Times apply to winter weeding and cleaning under the following conditions:

a. Plantations which have not been weeded for approximately 3 to 5 years, where the trees are generally above the level of grass and herbaceous weeds, but are suffering competition from bramble, briar, honeysuckle, clematis and woody weeds.

  N.B. Where plantations have not been weeded for one or two years, use the Standard Times for Weeding by Hand (XV No 1) increased according to para. 7 f of that table.

b. Weeds are cut in late winter or early spring when the grass and herbs are dead and do not need cutting.

c. Slopes up to 25% but see para. 7a.

d. Occasional loose stones and rough ground.

2. WORK SPECIFICATION

The Standard Times are for the following work:

a. Cut all climbers and woody weeds and lay them between rows.

b. Cut weeds to be kept clear of major drains, footpaths, etc.

3. TOOLS

Mixtures of climbers and woody weeds:- Light Brushing Hook or S - hook.

Mostly thick woody weeds:- Heavy Brushing Hook or S - hook.

4.   <u>ALLOWANCES</u>

(i)   <u>Included in Standard Times</u>

     a.   For contingencies and work other than the actual cutting, e.g. tool maintenance, breakdowns, walking between work sites, etc. 10% of the time spent cutting.

     b.   Personal needs and rest: 15% of the total working time.

(ii)   <u>To be included in price per Standard Minute</u>

     The appropriate incentive allowance.

5.   <u>METHOD OF SETTING THE RATE</u>

a)   Define:

     1)   The major weed groups present:

     C.   Climbers, mostly Bramble

     D.   Woody weeds (Coppice and seedlings)

     2)   The grade of difficulty of each group (see appendix)

     3)   The cover of each group as a percentage of the area to be cut, estimated in steps of 5%.

N.B.   The area may include a percentage of ground where weed growth is not competing with the crop and does not therefore require cutting. A time must however be allocated to these areas where it is impracticable to avoid walking them when cutting (see paragraph 6).

The following example shows how the assessment might look at this stage:

Weed Group	Grade	% Cover
Climbers	5	20%
Woody Weeds	4	20%
	5	30%
Bare Ground	–	30%
		100%

b. <u>Convert % cover and difficulty into Standard Time:</u>

(i)   Table 6 gives the Standard Times for cutting
      climbers and woody weeds. The times are listed
      according to the tree spacing, and the grade of
      difficulty. Look up the Standard Time for cutting
      one hectare of each weed group.

(ii) Multiply the times by the % cover.

(iii) Add together the times allocated to each weed group
      to find the Standard Time for weeding one hectare.

(iv) Example of weed assessment and calculation of
      Standard Time:

<u>Weed Assessment</u>

Major Weed Group	Grade	% cover	Standard Time per hectare ∅	% factor	Standard Time per hectare
Climbers	5	20%	4250	20%	850
Woody Weeds	4	20%	5580	20%	1116
Woody Weeds	5	30%	8170	30%	2451
Bare Ground	–	30%	200	30%	60
Total		100%			4477

∅ From Table 6,   1.5 m spacing

N.B. <u>Set rates for areas which will be weeded in one to six weeks</u>,
     <u>i.e. for relatively large blocks – whole compartments rather</u>
     <u>than small parts of compartments.</u>

6. WINTER WEEDING AND CLEANING BY HAND TOOLS — TIME PER HECTARE IN STANDARD MINUTES

WEED GROUP	GRADE	PLANT SPACING (metres)							
		2.1x2.1	2.0x2.0	1.9x1.9	1.8x1x8	1.7x1.7	1.6x1.6	1.5x1.5	1.4x1.4
C. CLIMBERS Principally Bramble,	4	2620	2710	2810	2900	3000	3100	3210	3310
Briar also Honeysuckle and	5	3460	3590	3720	3850	3980	4110	4250	4380
Clematis etc	6	4770	4970	5170	5370	5560	5760	5950	6130
D. WOODY WEEDS Coppice and Seedlings.	4	4500	4680	4860	5040	5220	5400	5580	5760
Gorse and Broom included	5	6570	6840	7110	7380	7640	7910	8170	8420
AREAS NOT REQUIRING ANY CUTTING (See 5a - 3)		150	155	160	170	180	190	200	210

NOTE: INTERPOLATE BETWEEN GRADES WHERE NECESSARY

J

7.   MODIFICATIONS AND VARIATIONS TO THE STANDARD TIMES

   N.B. These modifications should be applied at the Forester's
         discretion using his judgement as to the appropriateness
         of the conditions.

a. Allowance for steep slopes

    The Standard Times are for slopes up to 25%; on steeper
    slopes work is generally more difficult and it is usually
    necessary to work uphill only. The following additions may
    be made to the Standard Times:

Range of slope	% Increase in Standard Time
Over 25% – 35%	5%
Over 35% – 45%	10%
Over 45%	15%

b. Below average ground conditions

    Where ground conditions are very bad, e.g. steep slopes
    with unstable, stony surface; obstruction by windrows of
    slash or fallen boughs from ringed trees; ploughed sites
    where furrows are choked with gorse and bramble, etc.

                 ADD up to 20% in steps of 5%

c. Closed Canopy

    Where the canopy has closed or most branches have inter-
    laced and work is more difficult, Standard Times may be
    increased by 5% – 10%.

d. Less vigorous growth

    The following deductions from Standard Time may provide a
    guide for sites where weed growth is not so vigorous as the
    descriptions in the Appendix.

    Climbers: Use the Standard Times for Weeding by Hand
    (Grade C 3).

    Woody Weeds: Reduce the Standard Times for Grade D4 by
    10% to 20%.

WINTER WEEDING AND CLEANING BY HAND

ASSESSING THE DIFFICULTY

This appendix is a guide to assessing the difficulty of cutting climbers and woody weeds and allocating a Standard Time to the work.

Climbers

Three grades of difficulty are recognised - grades 4, 5 and 6. They may be regarded as Light, Moderate and Heavy respectively for the type of growth commonly found when weeding has not been done for several years; they are numbered 4 to 6 to distinguish them from grades 1 to 3 recognised in the annual weedings which are done in the first few years after planting and described in the appendix to the Standard Time Table for Hand Weeding (XV No. 1).

The assessment comprises two factors - firstly the density or number of stems to the square metre and secondly the growth characteristics of the climbers namely height, thickness, toughness, etc. It is the combination of these factors which indicates the grade.

Woody Weeds

Two grades, D4 and 5, additional to those used in hand weeding, are recognised in winter weeding and cleaning.

The characteristics described in these tables are intended as a guide and not as rigid rules for assessing weed growth. Reasonable tolerance should be allowed for the measurements given, in particular to height. Generally the density and toughness of stems are the most important factors which determine the cutting time.

Warning

Weed growth on former hardwood sites varies considerably from one locality to another. Foresters may find that even though there has been a gap of several years since the last weeding, the descriptions of weed growth and Standard Times given do not apply to their conditions. Similarly where coppice regrowth has been prevented or severely checked by chemical treatment of stumps the times may not apply. On such sites where for one reason or another climbers and woody weeds have not grown vigorously, the deductions from Standard Time indicated in paragraph 7d may provide a useful guide.

C. <u>CLIMBERS</u>. Bramble, Rosebriar, Raspberry Cane, Honeysuckle.
Several year's growth

Grade	Height	Thickness	Density of stems	General Description of factors indicating grade
4.	1–1.2m with occasional large runners	Up to 12 mm	Plants mostly 0.6–0.9m apart	Typical of sites not weeded for several years. Long runners entwined with trees and coppice.
5.	1–1.2m with runners up to 3m long	Up to 20mm	Plants mostly 0.3–0.6m apart	Bramble sometimes in waist high bushes. Honeysuckle forming occasional dense mats and climbing trees.
6.	1.2–1.5 m with runners often over 30m long	Mostly 20mm	Mostly under 0.3m apart	Often dense bushes up to shoulder height. Very difficult to push through before cutting. Long runners entwined amongst coppice stems making it difficult to cut freely. Multiple honeysuckle stems invading up to 50% of the trees.

<u>NOTE</u>: Raspberry cane forms dense patches. It is softer than bramble, does not bush so densely, and rarely justifies a grading of 3 or more.

D. COPPICE REGROWTH AND SEEDLING⌄. SEVERAL YEARS GROWTH. THICKNESS
CLASSIFICATION DEPENDS ON THE HEIGHT AT WHICH GROWTH IS TO BE CUT

Grade	Height	Thickness	Density of stems	General Description of Factors Indicating Grade
4. Very Heavy	Up to 3 metres but mostly in the range 1.2-2.5m	Up to 20mm	Stumps frequent. 30-40 shoots on most stumps	Many stems cut with one stroke using a heavy brushing hook or S-hook. On Coppice stools several stems cut with one stroke.
5.	Up to 4.5 metres but mostly in the range 2-4 metres	20-40 mm	Stumps very frequent. More than 40 shoots on many stumps	Including a small proportion of stems up to 5.0 cm diameter. Most stems require more than one cutting stroke.

NOTE:

WOODY WEEDS variations in toughness

Some species are much tougher and more difficult to cut than others,
eg Oak, Alder, Ash, Hazel, Broom and Gorse and where these comprise
the bulk of woody weed growth they may require a higher grading than
the more common mixture where softer species such as Willow, Sycamore,
Birch and Elder are included.

Section	XV
No	G1
Date	July 1971

<u>OUTPUT GUIDE</u>

<u>WEEDING WITH TRACTOR POWERED WEEDING MACHINES</u>

1.   <u>CONDITIONS</u>

The outputs apply to mechanical weeding under the following conditions:

    a.   Ground conditions

       (i)   slopes up to 20%.

      (ii)   less than 5 stumps, standing trees, or other obstacles per hectare causing delay or detour.

    (iii)   Ground surface providing reasonable traction.

    b.   Trees planted in reasonably parallel rows at 1.5m, 1.8m or 2.1 m row spacing.

    c.   Trees reasonably visible.

2.   <u>JOB SPECIFICATION</u>

The output guide applies to the following work:

    a.   Cut the appropriate width of weed growth (1.2m, 1.5m or 1.8 m) between the rows of trees at a height of 15–25 cm according to conditions.

    b.   Avoid damage to the planted crop.

    c.   Carry out maintenance on tractor and weeding machine as detailed in hand book and appendix II to this guide.

3.   <u>TOOLS AND EQUIPMENT</u>

    a.   Tractor and weeding machine, correctly modified and guarded, as appropriate to row spacing and weed growth.

b. Tractor fuel, oil etc. and all necessary tools, spares and other equipment as detailed in appendix III to this guide to be available at working site.

c. Protective clothing, ie safety helmet, ear protectors and gloves for operator.

4. **ALLOWANCES**

a. Contingencies and other work, 20% of cutting. (This includes maintenance of tractor and weeding machine, minor repairs of not more than 30 minutes accumulated duration during the day, clearing of odd obstructions from route and crossing drains with drain crossing bridges).

b. Rest allowance 20% of total work.

5. **SELECTING THE OUTPUT**

a. Ascertain the spacing between the rows

b. Estimate the percentage cover of the four weed groups as recognised for hand weeding. Because of the power of a machine, these can be condensed into two as follows:

VI covering groups A123, B123, C1 and 2 and D1.

V2 covering groups C3 and D2 and 3.

c. Measure the average length of run the machine will make before turning.

d. Using the figures from a, b and c above look up the output from the table in para 6.

6. **OUTPUT TABLE**

Output in hectares per 8 hour day.

Row Spacing	Vegetation	Average length "weeding run" in metres						
		Up to 55	60-95	100-135	140-175	180-215	220-255	260-295
1.5m	VI	1.56	1.96	2.16	2.28	2.34	2.40	2.46
1.5m	V2	1.31	1.59	1.72	1.80	1.83	1.86	1.90
1.8m	VI	1.83	2.36	2.60	2.74	2.82	2.91	2.91
1.8m	V2	1.56	1.93	2.07	2.16	2.21	2.26	2.26
2.1m	VI	2.18	2.77	3.03	3.18	3.36	3.36	3.42
2.1m	V2	1.83	2.23	2.40	2.49	2.59	2.59	2.64

Example

a.   Row spacing 1.5 m

b.   Average length of weeding run 80 m

c.   Weed assessment

Herbs A3, Grasses A2, Climbers C2   All into V1, percentage
cover = 60

Climbers C3, Woody weeds D2   All into V2, percentage
cover = 40

From output table:

Spacing 1.5 m, Vegetation V1 60%, weeding run 80 m, output
$\frac{1.96 \times 60}{100}$ = 1.18 ha

Spacing 1.5 m, Vegetation V2 40%, weeding run 80 m, output
$\frac{1.59 \times 40}{100}$ = 0.64 ha

Total
output   = 1.82 ha

7.   MODIFICATIONS AND VARIATIONS TO OUTPUTS

Note: These modifications and variations should be applied at
the foresters discretion using his judgement as to the
appropriateness of the condition.

a.   Obstacles

A percentage reduction in output per 10 obstacles per
hectare is necessary. An obstacle is defined as: a stump,
stone, pole, standing tree from previous crop, converging
row of trees, wet hole, mound, etc. likely to cause delay
or detour.

To make an allowance for these obstacles, firstly count the
number of obstacles per hectare and round to the nearest
10, then reduce the output figure obtained from the table
in para 6 by the percentage obtained from the graph in
Appendix I.

Example

From row spacing 2.1 m, weed assessment V2, weeding run
120 m, output from the table in para 6 = 2.40 ha per day.

Plate 47. The Horstine Farmery TMA 1 tractor mounted granule applicator fitted to a Massey Ferguson MF 135 agricultural tractor. WS 2/35/15

Plate 48. "Pharos" – the two-man version of this sledge mounted live-reel sprayer. WS 2/34/11

Plate 49. "Pharos" being used to spray cut stumps and basal bark. WS 2/34/10

Plate 50. 20-gallon (91 litre) fibre glass reservoir mounted on a stand (with adjustable legs) being used to fill a Policlair Mk I knapsack sprayer. WS 4/73

Plate 51. Drake and Fletcher "Victair" tractor mounted mistblower. WS 3/3/34

Plate 52. Live reel sprayer mounted on a trailer. WS 1/51/0

Plate 53. Allman high volume tractor mounted sprayer applying 2,4,5-T in oil to cut stumps.
WS 4/67

Plate 54. An experimental Allman tractor mounted sprayer (towing its own reserve supply) applying 2,4,5-T in oil to cut stumps and basal bark. WS 2/33/6

Plate 55. The same machine as shown in Plate 54 being used to apply paraquat. Guards made from washing up bowls are in use. WS 3/2/9

Plate 56. Chipmunk aircraft applying 2,4,5-T in water to woody weed growth in a conifer plantation at Wicken Wood, Hazelborough Forest, Northants. CS 17978

Plate 57. Aircraft cutting off herbicide as it reaches a ride. Note marker to right of aircraft. CS 17976

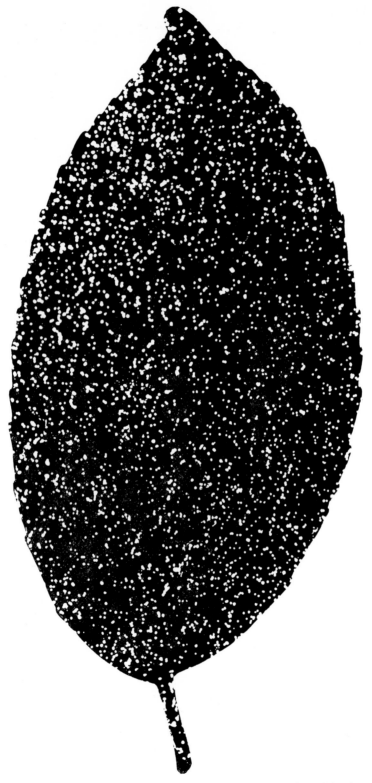

Plate 58. A leaf (at 1½ × magnification) showing the distribution of droplets applied by a ULV applicator and the evenness of the droplet size.

Plate 59. ULV portable sprayer powered by electric batteries. The operator is wearing provisionally recommended protective clothing. WS 5/1

Plate 60. A knapsack under development by which the range of the ULV hand applicator can be greatly increased. WS 3/10/29

Plate 61. The Turbair Tot, a hand carried, motorised fan-assisted ULV applicator.
WS 2/38/25

Obstacles per hectare to the nearest 10 is say, 30.

From the graph, using the output figure of 2.40 ha per day on the Y axis, the percentage reduction in output = 4.04% x 3 = 12.12%

Hence the corrected output = 240 − $\left(\dfrac{.240 \times 12.12}{100}\right)$ = 2.40−0.29

$$= 2.11 \text{ ha}$$

b. ## Poor visibility of trees

If the trees are difficult to see, reduce output in steps of 5% up to a maximum of 15%.

c. ## Very heavy woody weed growth

If the weed type is predominantly very heavy woody weed growth (ie it falls outside Category D3) decrease output by up to 25%.

APPENDIX I   to Table XV/G1

DECREASE IN OUTPUT FOR OBSTACLES IN WEEDING ROW

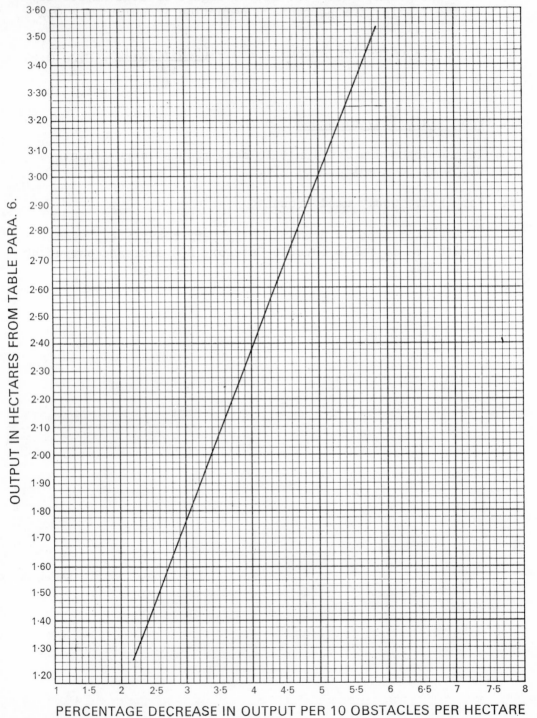

OUTPUT IN HECTARES FROM TABLE PARA. 6.

PERCENTAGE DECREASE IN OUTPUT PER 10 OBSTACLES PER HECTARE

APPENDIX II TO TABLE XV/G1

Brushcutter Maintenance

(See para 2c)

(i)   All nuts and bolts must be checked for tightness twice daily. The use of Loctite may help to reduce trouble from this source.

(ii) The gearbox oil level must be checked daily (140 EP oil)

(iii) All greasing points must be attended to daily (Note: on the Wolseley Swipe Jungle Buster, special attention is necessary to the greasing point for cutter shaft below gearbox)

(iv) The entire machine must be inspected daily for cracks and other damage.

(v)   The blades must be sharpened every one or two weeks according to weeding conditions.

APPENDIX III TO TABLE XV/G1

Tractor and Brushcutter Tools and Spares

(See para 3 b)

1. **Tractor Tools**

    All tractors should have a full set of the necessary spanners for
    the particular tractor concerned and should in addition have
    available on site the following items:

(i)	Adjustable spanner	(x)	3 tyre levers
(ii)	Pliers	(xi)	foot pump
(iii)	Screwdrivers (normal & Phillips)	(xii)	Puncture repair kit
(iv)	Block hammer		
(v)	Oil measure and can	(xiii)	Air pressure guage
(vi)	Funnel		
(vii)	Grease gun with flexible connector	(xiv)	Winch
(viii)	Hydraulic jack	(xv)	Ground anchor
(ix)	Wheel brace	(xvi)	Drain crossing bridges
		(xvii)	Spade
		(xviii)	Saw

2. **Brushcutter Tools**

    The tractor tool kit should serve for normal maintenance but the
    following additional items are necessary:

    1 11/16" A F socket for changing blades

    $1\frac{1}{8}$"   W   socket for changing dish

    $\frac{3}{4}$"   A F high lift ring spanner for gearbox retaining bolts.

    450 mm Stillson wrench

    $\frac{3}{4}$" Drive socket bar approx 22" (55cm) long.

    A torque spanner is necessary for periodic checks on the torque
    limiting clutch.

    For Wolseley Swipe Jungle Buster

    Allen keys for triangle fixing screws

    15/16" A F ring spanner

3. Brushcutter Spares

The following spares should be kept with the machine:

Blade Type machines

1 Dish, 2 sets of blades, 2 pivot bolts, nuts, spring washers and keys, 1 dish retaining nut.

Chain Type machines

1 set of chains, triangles and Allen screws.

Section	XV
No	G2
Date	August 1971

OUTPUT GUIDE

CHEMICAL WEEDING

FOLIAR SPRAYING WITH THE VICTAIR TRACTOR-MOUNTED MISTBLOWER

1. CONDITIONS

This guide refers to foliar spraying of hardwood regrowth in conifer plantations with aqueous solutions of 2,4,5-T under the following conditions:-

a. The average height of plantation trees and woody weeds not to exceed 2 m.

b. Racks to be cut at 10 m or 15 m spacings or tractor to travel over the top of one row of trees or between two rows

c. Drums or bowsers of diluent to be previously positioned conveniently for filling and refilling the mistblower.

2. JOB SPECIFICATION

This guide is for the following work:

a. Fill mistblower with self filling pump from drums or bowser

b. Travel to spraying site.

c. Spray.

d. Return to refill.

e. Occasional "in work" maintenance and adjust protective clothing.

Note: No allowance is made for setting out drums, travelling to the work site from depot, on/off protective clothing or daily tractor/mistblower maintenance.

3. ## TOOLS AND EQUIPMENT

a. Massey Ferguson 165 or equivalent tractor with cab. A
MF 135 tractor or its equivalent may be used if fitted with
from wheel weights.

b. Victair Standard mistblower as modified for forestry use.

c. Barrels, drums or bowsers set out at convenient intervals
containing diluted herbicide.

d. Protective clothing.

e. Washing facilities.

4. ## ALLOWANCES

a. Work other than that detailed in paragraphs 2. a-e is not
included in the job specification and should be paid for
separately.

b. No Relaxation Allowance is included as such. It is
considered that adequate rest can be taken during the
20 minutes refill time while the operator waits for the
machine to complete the job. This period is equivalent to
a minimum allowance of 20%.

5. ## SELECTING THE OUTPUT

a. Decide the appropriate application rate. If this falls
between 100 and 150 litres/ha interpolate as necessary.

b. From the density and height of the vegetation decide the
width of treatment. Normally this is 15m, but where
vegetation is over 2 m and/or very dense, a 10 m interval
may be adopted.

c. Carry out a trial run in the compartment to determine the
speed at which the tractor can be driven steadily.

d. Using these parameters, read the output from the table in
paragraph 6.

6.   <u>OUTPUT TABLE</u>

Tractor speed (km/h)	Output in hectares per hour			
	100 litres/ha		150 litres/ha	
	10 m strip	15 m strip	10 m strip	15 m strip
2	1.6	2.3	1.5	2.0
3	2.3	3.0	2.0	2.6
4	2.8	3.6	2.4	3.0

Section	XV
No	G3
Date	June 1972

OUTPUT GUIDE

CHEMICAL WEEDING

THE APPLICATION OF ATRAZINE IN THE FOREST

1.   CONDITIONS

The times apply to the application of atrazine under the
following conditions:

a.   The rows of trees must be easily visible (but see para 7c)

b.   The slope must be sufficiently gentle for an average
      walking speed of 2 mph (3.2 km/h) to be maintained (but
      see para 7b).

c.   Some brash, litter etc may be present providing that
      2 mph can be maintained.

d.   Water, in a bowser or 45 gallon drums, distributed with
      the herbicide to avoid excessive walking to refill (30
      metres maximum)but see paragraph 7a.

2.   JOB SPECIFICATION

The times apply to the following work:

a.   Spray the herbicide over the row of trees to give the
      desired width of 1 metre. The red polijet should be
      carried so that it is 25 cm above ground level and spraying
      vertically downwards.

b.   Walk at 2 mph when spraying (1 yard in 1 second).

c.   Weigh or measure the required amount of powder and mix
      thoroughly in water (currently 13 oz or 360 grammes in 18
      litres) immediately prior to using.

d.   Maintain the pressure on which the flow was calculated,
      eg to give a spraying time of $7\frac{1}{2}$–8 minutes per sprayer
      full.

K

e. Fill the sprayer to 18 litres.

f. Rinse out the sprayer with water at the end of each day.

g. Avoid spraying, or rinsing out, any herbicide into ditches, streams etc.

3. TOOLS AND EQUIPMENT

a. Cooper Pegler Policlair Mark II or CP III.

b. Red polijet, pressure control valve and gauge.

c. 21 inch or 28 inch lance.

d. Semi-rotary pump with barrel adaptor

e. Plastic bucket for mixing chemical powder and water.

f. Scoop for chemical powder marked to hold the desired amount (say 13 oz) or pre-measured sachets for each sprayer-full.

g. Protective clothing.

h. Washing facilities.

4. ALLOWANCES
    Included in the times

a. For contingencies and work other than cyclic time, eg mixing herbicide, on/off protective clothing, washing hands etc 17.5% of the time spent spraying.

b. For personal needs and rest, 22% of the total working time.

5. METHOD OF USING THE OUTPUT GUIDE

Paragraph 6 gives the time to spray one litre of herbicide; to convert this to output in hectares per day, divide the number of litres sprayed per day by the average sprayed volume per hectare.

6. TIME FOR APPLYING ATRAZINE

1.27 minutes per litre, assuming the sprayer to be filled with 18 litres.

7.   MODIFICATIONS AND VARIATIONS TO THE TIME

NB. These modifications should be applied at the Forester's
     discretion using his judgement as to the appropriateness
     of the conditions

a.   EXCESS WALKING

     Excess walking over 30 metres from chemical supply point to
     nearest point of spray area

     Add 0.1 minutes per litre for every additional 30 metres
     walked.

b.   STEEP SLOPES AND POOR GROUND CONDITIONS

     Where steep slopes or poor ground conditions make it
     impossible to maintain an average walking speed of 2 mph,
     it will be necessary to recalibrate the sprayer at the
     reduced walking speeds shown below.

     Add   0.32 minutes per litre at 1.5 mph.

     Add   0.64 minutes per litre at 1.0 mph.

c.   ROWS DIFFICULT TO FOLLOW

     Where rows are indistinct and cannot be easily followed

     Add up to 0.13 minutes per litre

d.   GROUND OBSTRUCTIONS

     Where there are obstructions to forward progress
     necessitating a detour on otherwise good ground conditions

     Add up to 0.13 minutes per litre.

e.   REDUCED QUANTITY CARRIED

     On very rare occasions it may not be possible or practical
     to carry a full sprayer.

     When the sprayer is $\frac{3}{4}$ full (13.5 litres)

     Add 0.11 minutes per litre

     When the sprayer is $\frac{1}{2}$ full (9 litres)

     Add 0.40 minutes per litre

f. SPOT SPRAYING

For spot spraying, the individual trees must be visible. An
area around the tree of 1 square metre should be treated.

Where the tree spacing in the row is 2 metres and over
Add 0.72 minutes per litre
Where the tree spacing in the row is under 2 metres
Add 0.36 minutes per litre.

APPENDIX TO TABLE XV/G3

CALIBRATION OF THE SPRAYER

1.   In order to achieve the desired quantity per hectare, the variables which affect the quantity of chemical applied to the hectare must be controlled.

    They are:

    A Proportion
    B Walking Speed
    C Spray width
    D Nozzle
    E Pressure

PROPORTION

2.   The proportion chosen is to mix 9 kg of powder in 450 litres of water for one <u>treated</u> hectare total coverage.

WALKING SPEED

3.   A comfortable walking speed over forest ground is 2 mph (3.22 km/h) equivalent to approximately 1 yard a second and is acceptable over all but the very easiest terrain or the steeper slopes.

SPRAY WIDTH

4.   A spray width of 1 metre gives adequate control except in areas of very tall vegetation (which are likely to be unsuitable for atrazine) or with very small trees.

NOZZLE

5.   A red polijet or politip gives an even flow of liquid over the whole band width.

PRESSURE

6.   With the above variables fixed, the pressure can then be calculated to give the desired flow. At 3.22 km/h (2mph) an operator will walk 3220 lineal metres in one hour. If spraying a band 1 metre wide the spray will cover an area of 3220 square metres.

With the quantity of liquid fixed at, in this example 450 litres per hectare, the spray will need to deliver:-

$$\frac{3220}{10000} \times 450 \quad = \quad \begin{array}{l} \text{145 litres per hour} \\ \text{or 2.4 litres per minute} \\ \text{or 1 litre in 25 seconds} \\ \text{or 18 litres in } 7\frac{1}{2} \text{ to 8 minutes.} \end{array}$$

With the sprayer on the operator's back and with his maintaining his normal pumping pressure, the pressure control valve must now be adjusted to give this flow. This can be measured precisely over a litre or two and checked over a full load. The pressure gauge will probably read between 12 and 16 p.s.i. depending on the gauge, but the rate of flow must be the criterion (ie 1 litre in 25 secs) rather than gauge pressure.

7.   Alternative rates of flow can be calculated by using other specifications, eg:

700 litres per hectare
Spray width of 1.2 metres
Walking speed of 3 mph.

Section	XV
No	G4
Date	Sept 1971

OUTPUT GUIDE

CHEMICAL WEEDING

THE APPLICATION OF GRANULAR HERBICIDES USING A HORSTINE FARMERY

MOTORISED KNAPSACK APPLICATOR

1. CONDITIONS

   a. The rows of trees and, for spot treatment, the individual trees readily visible.

   b. Slope and ground conditions such that a walking speed of 3.2 km/h (2mph) can be maintained.

   c. The herbicides, in 25kg bags or kegs, close to site.

2. JOB SPECIFICATION

   a. Walk between refill point and treatment site.

   b. Fill the hopper with one third of the contents of a 25 kg keg.

   c. Band Application – Distribute the herbicide over the trees maintaining the desired width (1 metre) and desired walking speed (3.2 km/h = 2mph = 1 yd per sec). – see para 6A.

   Spot Application – Distribute herbicide over the trees maintaining the desired width and length of treatment 'spots', 1 metre x 1 metre – see para 6B.

   d. Maintain the engine revolutions at maximum allowed and fully open the on/off lever while spraying.

   e. In damp weather check that the tube below the hopper does not become partially blocked.

3.   TOOLS AND EQUIPMENT

    a.   Horstine Farmery knapsack distributor with fishtail nozzle.
       If spot treatment is to be practised, a modified on/off
       handle is required.

    b.   Supply of 25:1 petrol, and filter funnel.

    c.   A stand of some sort to facilitate lifting the distributor
       on to the operator's back.

    d.   Plug spanner, screwdriver, carburettor spanner, adhesive
       tape, spare plugs.

    e.   Protective clothing.

    f.   Ear muffs (if desired).

    g.   Washing facilities.

4.   ALLOWANCES

In a full day, for operations other than cyclic work, 62 minutes
have been allowed. This is 19% of cyclic work. For personal
needs and rest, 96 minutes per day or 25% of total work have
been allowed.

5.   METHOD OF PREDICTING OUTPUT

Assess the distance between refill point and midway into the
area to be treated. Read off the output from para 6 below;
adjust output as appropriate if conditions specified in para 7
apply.

6.   TABLE OF OUTPUTS

These outputs can be expected given the conditions specified in
paragraph 1.

A   BAND APPLICATION

Average distance between refill point and midpoint of area to be treated (metres)	Output in full day	
	kgs	hectares (net)
50	80 – 90	1.3 – 1.45
100	75 – 85	1.2 – 1.35
150	70 – 80	1.15 – 1.3

B SPOT APPLICATION

Average distance between refill point and midpoint of area to be treated (metres)	Output in full day	
	kgs	hectares (net)
50	42 – 50	0.68 – 0.81
100	41 – 49	0.66 – 0.74
150	40 – 48	0.64 – 0.67

7. MODIFICATIONS AND VARIATIONS

N.B. The following modifications should be applied at the forester's discretion using his judgement as to the appropriateness of the conditions.

a. Obstacles and short rows

Where there are obstacles to avoid or short rows, output will be reduced, in relation to their significance by up to 10%.

Section	XV
Number	G5
Date	October 1972

<u>OUTPUT GUIDE</u>

<u>CHEMICAL WEEDING</u>

<u>THE APPLICATION OF HERBICIDES IN THE FOREST – SPOT SPRAYING</u>

<u>USING KNAPSACK SPRAYERS FITTED WITH A GUARD</u>

1.   <u>CONDITIONS</u>

The times apply to spraying under the following conditions:-

a.   Slopes up to 25%

b.   Occasional stones and rough ground

c.   Stumps and some litter from the previous crop

d.   Trees readily visible among the vegetation

e.   Adequate supplies of pre-mixed chemical solution distributed to avoid excessive walking to refill the sprayer (not more than 30 metres)

f.   Where conditions differ from those shown above, extra time may be required – see paragraph 7a.

2.   <u>JOB SPECIFICATION</u>

The times apply to the following work:-

a.   Spraying diluted herbicide (eg paraquat or dalapon) at a rate of 450 litres per treated hectare

b.   Walking to and from the spraying area to the bulk supply point

c.   Refilling knapsack sprayer from bulk container, washing out and regularly maintaining the sprayer.

3. <u>TOOLS AND EQUIPMENT</u>

   a. A Cooper Pegler CP III (Forest Model) or Policlair Mk II
       knapsack sprayer fitted with pressure control valve,
       pressure gauge and guard. The sprayer to operate at a
       pressure of between 0.28 kg/cm^2 and 0.42 kg/cm^2 (4-6 p. s. i.)

       <u>NB.The guard can contain either the tree (eg Politec,
       Policone) or the nozzle (eg Cooper Pegler internal spray
       shield, washing up bowl etc)</u>

   b. Either a bowser or drum(s) for the supply of pre-mixed
       herbicide

   c. Protective clothing

   d. Washing facilities.

4. <u>ALLOWANCE</u>

   Included in the times:-

   a. For contingencies and work other than that included in the
       cyclic time, eg maintenance, on/off protective clothing,
       washing hands etc,7% of the time spent spraying.

   b. For personal needs and rest,25% of the total working time.

5. <u>METHOD OF USING THE OUTPUT GUIDE</u>

   Paragraph 6 gives the time per hectare against plant spacing
   and the type of guard being used.

   <u>Example:</u>

   An area of 1.2 metres around each tree in a compartment planted
   at 2.1 m x 2.1 m spacing is to be sprayed with paraquat using a
   guarded nozzle. Conditions are as stated in paragraph 1.

   Time per hectare = 398 standard minutes.

6. TIME PER HECTARE IN STANDARD MINUTES

TREE SPACING IN METRES	NUMBER OF TREES PER HECTARE	STANDARD MINUTES PER HECTARE							
		USING TREE GUARD		USING GUARDED NOZZLE					
		0.9 m * (42 cc)	litres applied per ha	0.9 m * (42 cc)	litres applied per ha	1.2 m * (63 cc)	litres applied per ha	1.5 m * (84 cc)	litres applied per ha
1.4 x 1.4	5102	742	214	557	214	693	321	767	429
1.5 x 1.5	4444	689	187	524	187	646	280	717	373
1.6 x 1.6	3906	639	164	491	164	601	246	670	328
1.7 x 1.7	3460	588	145	461	145	558	218	626	291
1.8 x 1.8	3086	540	130	430	130	517	194	583	259
1.9 x 1.9	2770	492	116	401	116	477	175	542	233
2.0 x 2.0	2500	445	105	373	105	437	158	501	210
2.1 x 2.1	2268	398	95	344	95	398	143	465	191

* Diameter of the area treated around each tree (equivalent dosage per tree in brackets)

FOOTNOTE :

Where tree spacings are other than those shown above, entry to the table should be made using the appropriate number of trees per hectare and interpolating where necessary.

7. MODIFICATIONS AND VARIATIONS TO THE TIMES

NB <u>These modifications and variations should be applied at the Forester's discretion using his judgement as to the appropriateness of the conditions</u>

a. <u>Poor ground conditions</u>

Where ground conditions are worse than those shown under paragraph 1, eg lop and top from previous crop not burnt, fallen boughs from ringed trees, mine-workings, unstable slopes etc

<u>ADD</u> up to 20% in steps of 5%

b. <u>Steep slopes</u>

On slopes steeper than 25% add to the times as follows:-

Slope	% Increase
Over 25% - 35%	5%
Over 35% - 45%	10%
Over 45%	15%

c. <u>Excess walking</u>

On sites where it is not possible to position the refill point within 30 metres of the spraying area

<u>ADD</u> 0.1 standard minutes per litre sprayed for every additional 30 metres walked.

d. <u>Allowance for moving semi-rotary pump, stand and hose</u>

When chemical solution is being supplied from a trailer/tank or drum by means of a semi-rotary pump and is required to be repositioned periodically

<u>ADD</u> 5%

e. <u>Small trees</u>

Where trees are small and difficult to find under dense cover:-

(i) Conifers in Herbs and Hardwoods in Grasses
<u>ADD</u> up to a maximum of 10%

(ii) Conifers in Grasses and Hardwoods in Herbs
<u>ADD</u> up to a maximum of 20%

Section	XV
Number	G6
Date	April 1972

OUTPUT GUIDE

CHEMICAL WEEDING

THE APPLICATION OF HERBICIDES IN THE FOREST — FOLIAGE SPRAYING WITH

50% 2,4,5-T IN WATER USING KNAPSACK SPRAYERS

1.   CONDITIONS

The times apply to foliage spraying under the following conditions:-

a.   Pre or post-planting areas.

b.   All foliage to be readily accessible for spraying, plantations to be racked if necessary.

c.   Slopes up to 25%

d.   Occasional brash, litter, drains and rough ground.

e.   Adequate supplies of pre-mixed chemical solution distributed to avoid excessive walking to re-fill, (30 metres maximum) but see paragraph 7 a.

2.   JOB SPECIFICATION

The times are for the following work:-

a.   Apply herbicide to leaf surface of unwanted weed species, avoiding planted trees as far as possible.

b.   Walk to and from spray area to diluent container.

c.   Refill knapsack sprayer from container, wash out and regularly maintain.

3. <u>TOOLS AND EQUIPMENT</u>

    a. Cooper Pegler Cp III or Policlair Mark II knapsack sprayer fitted with pressure control valve and pressure guage, with pressure set at 0.70 kg/cm^2 (10 p.s.i.).

    b. 53 cm (21") or 71 cm (28") hand lance with red polijet or politip or brass PP 78 floodjet.

    c. No. 1 semi-rotary pump with barrel adapter or alkathene hose.

    d. Protective clothing.

    e. Washing facilities.

4. <u>ALLOWANCES</u>

<u>Included in the Times</u>

    a. For contingencies and work other than cyclic time, eg on/off protective clothing, washing hands etc, 7% of the time spent spraying.

    b. For personal needs and rest, 25% of the total working time.

5. <u>METHOD OF USING THE OUTPUT GUIDE</u>

Paragraph 6 gives the time to spray one litre of herbicide. To convert this to output in hectares per day, divide the number of litres sprayed per day by the average sprayed volume per hectare obtained by calibration runs.

6. <u>TIME FOR SPRAYING FOLIAGE</u>

The time per litre for applying a sprayer full of herbicide is 1.0 minutes.

7. <u>MODIFICATIONS AND VARIATIONS TO THE TIME</u>

NB <u>These modifications should be applied at the Forester's discretion using his judgement as to the appropriateness of the conditions</u>

    a. Excess walking over 30 metres from chemical supply point to nearest point of spray area.

    <u>Add</u> 0.1 minutes per litre for every additional 30 metres walked.

b. GROUND CONDITIONS

Where obstructions to walking are more than are normally
present on a forest floor, eg lop and top from previous
crops, fallen branches from ringed trees, mine workings,
unstable slopes, poor racks etc.

Add up to 20% in steps of 5%

c. SLOPE

The time in paragraph 6 is for slopes of up to 25%. On
steeper slopes increase the time as follows:-

	Slope		Add
Over 25%	-	35%	5%
Over 35%	-	45%	10%
Over 45%			15%

d. MOVING SEMI-ROTARY PUMP, STAND AND HOSE

When chemical solution is being supplied from a
trailer/tank or drum by means of a semi-rotary pump and
barrel adapter or alkathene hose, this has to be re-
positioned periodically.

Add 5%

Section	XV
No	G7
Date	Apr 72

OUTPUT GUIDE

CHEMICAL WEEDING

THE APPLICATION OF HERBICIDES IN THE FOREST –

SPRAYING HERBICIDES WITH KNAPSACK MISTBLOWERS

1.   CONDITIONS

The times apply to mistblowing chemical solutions under the
following conditions:

a.   Slopes up to 25%

b.   Occasional loose stones, rough ground and stumps and litter
     from racking.

c.   In overhead cover, bramble, dense grass or coppice,
     rackways will be provided

d.   Adequate supplies of pre-mixed chemical solution,
     distributed to avoid excessive walking to refill (30 metres
     maximum) but see paragraph 7a

2.   JOB SPECIFICATION

The times are for the following work:

a.   Applying mist to areas of all unwanted weed species (as
     directed by the supervisor)

b.   Filling mistblower container and fuel tank, washing out,
     cleaning and regular maintenance.

c.   Mechanical breakdowns of less than 15 minutes.

L

3.   <u>TOOLS AND EQUIPMENT</u>

    a.   Mistblower: Stihl SG 17; Wambo S 170a; Danarm W 170; KEF
        Motoblo 35; Cooper Pegler CP 40; Allman L 35

    b.   Fuel for mistblower, filter funnel, spare sparking plug,
        starter cord (where applicable), plug spanner, screwdriver,
        instruction book, water for cleaning mistblower and a
        supply of rag or cotton waste

    c.   No 1 semi-rotary pump with barrel adaptor or alkathene hose

    d.   Protective clothing

    e.   Washing facilities

4.   <u>ALLOWANCES</u>
    <u>Included in the times</u>

    a.   For contingencies and work other than actual mistblowing
        eg. maintenance, breakdowns of up to 15 minutes, refilling,
        refuelling, on/off protective clothing, cleaning machine
        and washing hands, 25% of the time spent mistblowing

    b.   For personal needs and rest, 25% of the total working time

5.   <u>METHOD OF SELECTING THE TIME</u>

    From a calibration run, determine the average rate of applica-
    tion and the jet size or nozzle setting to be used.

    <u>Example</u>

    Using a Wambo S 170 mistblower, calibration runs have determined
    that at nozzle setting $\frac{1}{4}$, the volume sprayed per hectare is 224
    litres. Paragraph 6 gives the time per litre of 4.0 minutes and
    an output per day of 120 litres.

    Output in hectares per day can be calculated by dividing the
    appropriate value in column 7 of paragraph 6 by the number of
    litres sprayed per hectare as determined by the calibration run.

    eg. $\dfrac{120 \text{ litres per day}}{224 \text{ litres per hectare}}$ = .54 hectares per day

6. <u>TIME FOR MISTBLOWING</u>

Jet size or nozzle marking					Minutes per Litre	Output in Litres per Day
CP 40	KEF Motoblo 35	Allman L 35	Danarm W 170 Wambo S 170a	Stihl SG 17		
–	1	2	–	–	5.3	91
2	–	–	$\frac{1}{4}$	–	4.0	120
3	–	–	–	–	3.1	155
–	–	3	–	1	2.6	185
4	2	–	–	–	2.2	218
–	–	–	–	–	2.0	240
5	–	4	$\frac{1}{2}$	$1\frac{1}{2}$	1.8	267

NB. With the Allman L 35, Stihl SG 17, Wambo S 170a and
    Danarm W 170 mistblowers only, it is possible to set
    the output control between the values marked. The
    output volume can be determined by calibration runs
    and the times interpolated.

7. <u>MODIFICATIONS AND VARIATIONS TO THE TIMES</u>

    NB. <u>These modifications should be applied at the forester's
         discretion using his judgement as to the appropriateness
         of the conditions</u>.

    a. <u>EXCESS WALKING</u>

        For walking over 30 metres from chemical supply point to
        the nearest point of spray area

                <u>ADD</u> 0.1 mins per litre for every additional
                30 metres walked

    b. <u>GROUND CONDITIONS</u>

        Where obstructions to walking are more than normally
        present on a forest floor, eg. lop and top from previous
        crop, fallen branches from ringed trees, mine workings,
        unstable slopes, poor racks etc.

                <u>ADD</u> up to 20% in steps of 5%

c. SLOPE

The times are for slopes up to 25% On steeper slopes

Increase the time per litre as shown below

Slope	Add
Over 25% – 35%	5%
Over 35% – 45%	10%
Over 45%	15%

d. ALLOWANCE FOR USING SEMI-ROTARY PUMP, STAND AND HOSE

When the herbicide is supplied from a trailer/tank or drum by means of a semi-rotary pump and alkathene hose and this requires to be re-positioned periodically, the time per litre may be increased by 5%.

Section	XV
Number	G8
Date	Feb 1973

OUTPUT GUIDE

CHEMICAL WEEDING, CLEANING AND PREP GROUND –

CUT STUMP AND BASAL BARK TREATMENT WITH

100% 2,4,5–T IN PARAFFIN USING

A. KNAPSACK SPRAYERS OR B. PHAROS (LIVE REEL SPRAYER)

1.   CONDITIONS

The Times apply under the following conditions:

a.   All stumps, poles or coppice to be readily accessible ie reasonable walking conditions, some bramble, brash, drains and rough ground. (See paragraph 7b)

b.   Bark to be dry at the time of spraying.

c.   Slopes up to 25% (See paragraph 7c)

d.   Required amount of chemical/oil to be available in a bowser or 45 gallon drums at operating positions at not more than 30 metres from the spraying area. (See paragraph 7a)

e.   With Pharos: a two or four man team.

2.   JOB SPECIFICATION

The Times are for the following work:

a.   Spray all cut stumps to saturate the whole stump surface to run–off.

b.   Spray all standing poles/coppice as required to saturate the bark over the full circumference of the stem from a height of 30 centimetres to ground level.

c. Spray with rose (solid stream) jet at 5 p s i.

KNAPSACK SPRAYER ONLY

d. Walk from spraying site to container to refill

e. Refill knapsack sprayer from container by semi-rotary pump

PHAROS ONLY

f. Spray area (see a and b above) including hauling out main hose and handling side lines.

g. Maintain Pharos.

N.B.   THE TIMES DO NOT INCLUDE THE FOLLOWING WORK (SEE PARA 7)

1. Prepare and set up Pharos for spraying. (7d)

2. Move Pharos as required to next spraying area. (7c)

3. Reel in and pack up on completion of spraying for the day, (7f)

3.   TOOLS AND EQUIPMENT

a. Knapsack sprayer (18 litres capacity), Cooper Pegler Policlair Mk II or CP III (Forestry model).

OR

b. Mk III Pharos

150 metre main line

3 metre suction and return hoses

2 x 37 metre side lines

Y piece fitted with self-sealing couplings

Tool box, tools and spares

Operators instruction book

The following additional equipment will be required when Pharos is used by a four-man team.

Three-way (X) junction

2 side lines and lances

25 and 6 metre extension hoses

c.   Pressure control valve and gauge

d.   21 inch or 28 inch lance

e.   No 250 nozzle and rose jet (5 x .040" solid stream disc)

f.   No 1 semi-rotary pump and barrel adaptor. (Knapsack sprayer only)

g.   Protective clothing and safety equipment

h.   Washing facilities.

ALLOWANCES

Included in the times :-

KNAPSACK SPRAYERS

a.   For contingencies and work other than spraying, walking and refilling, ie maintenance on/off protective clothing, washing hands etc.

> 15% of the cyclic time.

b.   For personal needs and rest

> 25% of the total working time.

PHAROS

a.   For contingencies and work other than spraying, walking and handling hose

> 17% of the cyclic time.

b.   For personal needs and rest

> 17% of the total working time.

5.   ## METHOD OF USING THE OUTPUT GUIDE

a.   Paragraph 6 A deals with prep ground using either knapsack sprayers or Pharos. Entry to the tables is based on an estimate of the volume of liquid applied per hectare. The time to apply 1 litre of herbicide, the time per hectare and the output in litres per hour are given.

b.   Paragraph 6 B deals with weeding or cleaning using either knapsack sprayers or Pharos. Table layout is as outlined in 5a above.

EXAMPLE

a. Prep ground

b. Knapsack sprayer

c. Slope 30% - other conditions as shown in paragraph 1.

d. Rate of herbicide application - 400 litres per hectare.

STANDARD MINUTE PER LITRE	=	2.11 (From paragraph 6 A (i))
Add 5% for slope	=	0.11 (From paragraph 7c)
Total time per litre	=	2.22 standard minutes
STANDARD MINUTES PER HECTARE	=	844 (From paragraph 6 A(i))
Add 5% for slope	=	42 (From paragraph 7c)
Total time per hectare	=	886 standard minutes
OUTPUT IN LITRES PER HOUR	=	28.4 (From paragraph 6 A(i))
Subtract 5% for slope	=	1.4 (From paragraph 7c)
Total output	=	27.0 litres per hour

6 A PREP GROUND

Time to spray 1 litre of herbicide, time to spray 1 hectare
with herbicide and output in litres per hour.

(i) KNAPSACK SPRAYER

LITRES APPLIED PER HECTARE	STANDARD MINUTES PER LITRE	STANDARD MINUTES PER HECTARE	OUTPUT IN LITRES PER HOUR
300	2.39	717	25.1
400	2.11	844	28.4
500	1.95	975	30.8
600	1.85	1110	32.4
700	1.79	1253	33.5
800	1.75	1400	34.3
900	1.71	1539	35.1

NB INTERPOLATE WHERE NECESSARY

Plate 62. The motorised fan-assisted ULV applicator mounted on a one-wheeled carriage for towing through the forest.

Plate 63. Tractor mounted dual ULV applicator. WS 4/72

Plate 64. Tractor mounted single oscillating fan ULV applicator.

Plate 65. 250-gallon trailer/bowser used for transporting diluted herbicide. WS 2/41/4

Plate 66. Light trailer fitted with 250-gallon (1136 litre) tank. There is also space for carrying equipment. WS 4/2/6

Plate 67. Locally made platform for fitting to 3-point linkage of MF 35. It is useful for carrying herbicide/diluent, etc. Side view. WS 2/73/37

Plate 68. Rear view of platform shown in Plate 67. WS 2/73/36

Plate 69. 250-gallon (1136 litre) polythene tank made locally showing the method of emptying by semi-rotary pump mounted on stake. WS 2/6/13A

Plate 71. Detail of corner fitting. WS 2/6/15A

Plate 70. Detail of stack pipe and hose coupling.
WS 2/6/14A

Plate 72. 600-gallon (2728 litre) polythene tanks beside road in Lincolnshire. WS 2/18/25

Plate 73. No. 1 Semi-rotary pump mounted on stake showing fittings necessary. WS 2/19/18

Plate 74. Barrel adaptor with semi-rotary pump used to empty 45-gal (205 litre drum). The drum is used as a stand for the sprayer. WS 2/50/13

Plate 75. A handy portable tripod refilling stand made from three stakes. WS 4/1/1

Plate 76. Drum carriers being used to transport a 45-gal (205 litre) drum of diluted herbicide into the compartment. WS 2/19/20

Plate 77. Detail of the drum carriers. WS 2/14/28

Plate 78. The Baxter 'Pneuseal' respirator for use with water-borne high/medium volume, low pressure sprays. WS 2/17/20

Plate 79. The Protector 'Toxigard' respirator for use with oil-borne sprays, mistblowers and aerial spraying. WS 2/17/18

Plate 80. Squares of black polythene in place during trials of this material as a weed suppressor at Tiptree Wood, Lavenham Forest, Essex. WS 4/14

(ii) PHAROS

LITRES APPLIED PER HECTARE	STANDARD MINUTES PER LITRE	STANDARD MINUTES PER HECTARE	OUTPUT IN LITRES PER HOUR
300	2.06	618	29.1
400	1.83	732	32.8
500	1.68	840	35.7
600	1.59	954	37.7
700	1.52	1064	39.5
800	1.47	1176	40.8
900	1.44	1296	41.7

NB INTERPOLATE WHERE NECESSARY

6B WEEDING OR CLEANING

Time to spray 1 litre of herbicide, time to spray 1 hectare with herbicide and output in litres per hour.

(i) KNAPSACK SPRAYER

LITRES APPLIED PER HECTARE	STANDARD MINUTES PER LITRE	STANDARD MINUTES PER HECTARE	OUTPUT IN LITRES PER LITRE
300	2.68	804	22.4
400	2.38	952	25.2
500	2.16	1080	27.8
600	2.03	1218	29.6
700	1.95	1365	30.8
800	1.90	1520	31.6
900	1.86	1674	32.3

NB INTERPOLATE WHERE NECESSARY

(ii) PHAROS

LITRES APPLIED PER HECTARE	STANDARD MINUTES PER LITRE	STANDARD MINUTES PER HECTARE	OUTPUT IN LITRES PER HOUR
300	2.34	702	25.6
400	2.06	824	29.1
500	1.87	935	32.1
600	1.76	1056	34.1
700	1.68	1176	35.7
800	1.63	1304	36.8
900	1.59	1431	37.7

NB INTERPOLATE WHERE NECESSARY

7.   MODIFICATIONS AND VARIATIONS TO THE TIMES AND OUTPUTS

N.B.   THESE MODIFICATIONS AND VARIATIONS SHOULD BE APPLIED AT
THE FORESTER'S DISCRETION USING HIS JUDGMENT AS TO THE
APPROPRIATENESS OF THE CONDITIONS

a.   EXCESS WALKING

On sites where it is not possible to position the refill
point for knapsack sprayers within 30 metres of the
spraying area

ADD   0.1 minutes per litre for every additional
30 metres walked.

b.   GROUND CONDITIONS

Where ground conditions are worse than those shown in
paragraph 1a and there are more obstructions to walking
eg lop and top left from previous crop, large boulders,
mine-workings, fallen boughs from ringed trees etc.

ADD   up to 20%, in steps of 5% to the times and
reduce the outputs by a similar amount.

c.   SLOPE

When slopes are steeper than 25% increase the times or
reduce the output as follows:

Slope	% Increase in time (or reduction in output)
Over 25% – 35%	5%
Over 35% – 45%	10%
Over 45%	15%

d.   PREPARE AND SET UP PHAROS AT COMMENCEMENT OF SPRAYING

ALLOW   10 minutes per man.

e.   MOVE PHAROS

On completion of spraying in a stint, when main line is
reeled in and Pharos moved normal distance of 60 metres

ALLOW   20 minutes per man.

Where the length of the spraying stint is over 130 metres,
additional time is required to walk back to Pharos and haul
in the main line.

ALLOW   25 minutes per man.

f. <u>PACK UP PHAROS AT THE END OF THE WORKING PERIOD</u>

   ALLOW   10 minutes per man.

Section	XV
Number	G9
Date	February 1973

OUTPUT GUIDE

CHEMICAL WEEDING –

THE APPLICATION OF HERBICIDES IN THE FOREST –

TREE INJECTION USING A SWEDISH WATER PISTOL AND A BOY SCOUT AXE

1.   CONDITIONS

The output guide applies to the application of herbicides by Swedish water pistol tree injector and Boy Scout axe under the following conditions:

a.   Diluted herbicide is available in easily transportable containers, eg 5 or 20 litre (1 or 5 gallon) drums.

b.   The ground conditions are classified under one of the three categories shown below:

EASY – clear floor; no restriction to movement, some light bramble.

MODERATE – some restriction to movement but not enough to warrant extensive racking. Condition between easy and difficult.

DIFFICULT – typical 'cleaning' situation. Heavy growth of coppice and bramble under light overhead shade.

c.   In the densest areas, racks to be provided every 3 to 5 rows.

d.   The trees to be injected should have stems individually accessible to the injector and have diameters at the injection point of between 7.5 and 20 cms.

e.   The density of trees to be injected not to exceed 1000 stems per hectare.

2. <u>JOB SPECIFICATION</u>

The output guide applies to the following work:

a. Cuts are to be placed at 75 mm centres on birch and
    susceptible species and 50 mm centres on moderately
    resistant species such as hazel and oak.

b. The dose per cut to be 1 millilitre of diluted herbicide.

c. Injections to reach the outer sapwood and to be made at
    a convenient height on the tree (can be at waist level).

3. <u>TOOLS AND EQUIPMENT</u>

a. One Fickningsspruta water pistol with the jet bored out
    to 2mm (1/16") diameter and equipped with a 2.5 litres
    ($\frac{1}{2}$ gallon) reservoir.

b. One Boy Scout axe (such as Spearwell type 3101).

c. One belt.

d. One sharpening stone.

e. One filter funnel.

f. One calibrated measuring vessel for filling the reservoir
    or for mixing herbicide and diluent.

g. Safety equipment and protective clothing

4. <u>ALLOWANCES</u>

Included in the output guide.

a. For contingencies and work other than actually injecting,
    eg. sharpening axe etc, 8% of the injecting time.

b. For personal needs and rest, 16% of the total working time.

5.   METHOD OF USING THE OUTPUT GUIDE

    a. Estimate the number of trees to be treated per hectare and assess the average girth in millimetres per tree at the injection point.

    b. Divide the average girth by either 75 (for birch and all susceptible species) or by 50 (for oak and all resistant species) to give the number of cuts per tree.

    c. Assess the ground conditions under the scale shown in paragraph 1b.

    d. Entry to the tables is gained by using the number of trees to be treated per hectare, the average number of cuts to be made per tree and the ground conditions.

EXAMPLE 1

Birch on easy ground conditions.

a. Number of trees per hectare – 600

b. Average girth – 300 millimetres

c. Number of cuts per tree equals $\dfrac{300}{75} = 4$

From paragraph 6A the time per litre is 111 standard minutes.
OR
From paragraph 6B the time per tree is 0.44 standard minutes.

EXAMPLE 2

Where unwanted trees occur in mixture, the following method of assessing the time may be used:

MODERATE GROUND CONDITIONS	BIRCH	OAK
a. Number of trees per hectare	600	400
b. Average girth	300 mm	400 mm
Therefore total girth per hectare	180,000 mm	160,000 mm
c. Divide by factor for number of cuts	75	50
Therefore number of cuts per hectare	2,400	3,200
d. Total number of cuts for both species	5,600	
e. Total number of trees for both species	1,000	
f. Average number of cuts per tree equals 5.6		

From paragraph 6A the time per litre is 105 standard minutes.

OR

from paragraph 6B the time per tree is 0.59 standard minutes.

6. A. <u>TIME IN STANDARD MINUTES TO APPLY 1 LITRE OF HERBICIDE</u>

Average No of cuts per tree	NUMBER OF TREES PER HECTARE								
	EASY CONDITIONS			MODERATE CONDITIONS			DIFFICULT CONDITIONS		
	1000	600	300	1000	600	300	1000	600	300
3	111	119	132	120	132	150	147	165	200
4	107	111	119	115	122	135	132	145	175
5	102	105	112	108	114	123	123	134	154
6	97	100	107	103	108	116	115	124	141
7	93	96	102	98	93	109	109	115	132
8	90	93	97	94	99	104	104	110	124
9	87	89	94	90	94	100	100	105	116
10	83	86	89	87	90	95	95	100	110
11	80	82	85	84	87	91	91	95	104
12	78	79	82	81	83	87	87	91	99
13	75	76	78	77	79	83	83	87	94
14	72	73	75	74	75	79	79	83	90
15	68	69	73	71	73	76	76	79	86
16	65	66	71	69	71	73	73	75	82

INTERPOLATE WHERE NECESSARY

6. B. <u>TIME IN STANDARD MINUTES TO TREAT ONE TREE</u>

Average No of cuts per tree	NUMBER OF TREES PER HECTARE								
	EASY CONDITIONS			MODERATE CONDITIONS			DIFFICULT CONDITIONS		
	1000	600	300	1000	600	300	1000	600	300
3	0.33	0.36	0.40	0.36	0.40	0.45	0.44	0.50	0.60
4	0.43	0.44	0.48	0.46	0.49	0.54	0.53	0.58	0.70
5	0.51	0.52	0.56	0.54	0.57	0.61	0.61	0.67	0.77
6	0.58	0.60	0.64	0.62	0.65	0.70	0.69	0.74	0.85
7	0.65	0.67	0.71	0.69	0.72	0.76	0.76	0.80	0.92
8	0.72	0.74	0.78	0.75	0.79	0.83	0.83	0.88	0.99
9	0.78	0.80	0.85	0.81	0.85	0.90	0.90	0.94	1.04
10	0.83	0.86	0.89	0.87	0.90	0.95	0.95	1.00	1.10
11	0.88	0.90	0.93	0.92	0.96	1.00	1.00	1.04	1.14
12	0.94	0.95	0.98	0.97	1.00	1.04	1.04	1.09	1.19
13	0.98	0.99	1.01	1.00	1.03	1.08	1.08	1.13	1.22
14	1.00	1.02	1.05	1.04	1.05	1.11	1.11	1.16	1.26
15	1.02	1.03	1.09	1.06	1.09	1.14	1.14	1.19	1.29
16	1.04	1.06	1.14	1.10	1.14	1.17	1.17	1.20	1.31

INTERPOLATE WHERE NECESSARY

7. <u>MODIFICATIONS AND VARIATIONS TO THE TIMES</u>

a. If regrowth from the unwanted stems has to be cut before injection can take place, extra time will be required.

Printed in England for Her Majesty's Stationery Office by Wells KPL Swindon Press, Swindon, Wilts

Dd. 504024 K44 5/74